Seasons of Change

OLD BARN & CORN CRIB
Arva, Ontario

Seasons of Change

SKETCHES OF LIFE ON THE FARM

TEXT BY DAVID DENSMORE

ARTWORK BY
GEORGE RICKARD
MARTHA ROBINSON
KARY SURONEN
LOUISE TAYLOR

Summerhill Press Ltd./Etue & Company Inc.

Toronto

Published by:
Summerhill Press Ltd./Etue & Company Inc.
Five Clarence Square
Toronto, Ontario M5V 1H1

Distribution:
Etue & Company Inc. is the exclusive agent for all sales outside of bookstore and libraries.

Editors: Bill Dimmick, Ian Coutts
Artists: George Rickard, Martha Robinson, Kary Suronen, Louise Taylor
Typesetting: Q Composition Inc., Toronto
Cover Design: Brian Moore, Design Force Inc.

Canadian Cataloguing in Publication Data
Densmore, David, 1948–
    Seasons of change

ISBN 0-920197-41-8

1. Family farms – Canada.   2. Farm life – Canada –
History.   I. Title.

S451.5A1D45 1987   631′.0971   C87-094409-6

The publisher would like to thank the assistance given by the United Cooperatives of Ontario in the development and production of this book.

Printed and bound in Canada by T.H. Best Co., Toronto

CONTENTS

Acknowledgements

The people to whom I am indebted for their help in writing this book are almost too numerous to mention. First and foremost, however, I must thank Elizabeth Etue and Jim Williamson for their gambling instincts in trusting me with such an important enterprise. The library and archives staff of the Ontario Agricultural Museum in Milton were more than generous in allowing me to intrude upon their busy schedules. Lynn Campbell, in particular, gave generously of her time, both to read and criticize the manuscript; her knowledge of agricultural technology is formidable. Thanks also to the Curator, Peter Ledwith, for checking the sketches.

The staffs of the Ontario Archives and of the University of Guelph's Photographic Services Division greatly aided me in my picture research. My editor, Bill Dimmick of *Farm and Country*, patiently answered all my queries, and helped keep this book in proper perspective at all times, while Ian Coutts did a masterful job of copy editing.

Finally, I owe my gratitude to my wife, Sandra, not only for her constant optimism and support, but also for her willingness to undertake the massive job of typing and retyping a flawed manuscript. What I owe to her, only she will ever know.

INTRODUCTION

Why would anyone try to chronicle 100 years of agricultural life in a province as large and diverse as Ontario? After all, when ninety-six percent of the population thinks of Ontario, rural life, farming and agricultural progress do not immediately come to mind. Most people probably think of big-city banking, auto manufacturing and the steel industry long before they ever consider farms and farming as significant in the life of this province.

Yet scratch a Toronto banker, an Oshawa assembly-line worker or a steelmaker from Hamilton and chances are you'll uncover someone with agricultural roots just beneath the surface. No more than two or three generations ago his family probably farmed in one of our counties. Many native Ontarians as well as recent immigrants are descendants of farmers, and perhaps unknowingly, inheritors of a rural tradition. We may not have lived or worked on a farm ourselves, but the sights, sounds and smells of farming are still our legacy, no matter how sophisticated or urbane we think we are. Farming remains the life-blood of a province steeped in agricultural tradition.

Seasons of Change examines a way of life that is at the same time both foreign to me and inextricably part of me, a heritage I have consciously ignored most of my life. My own paternal grandfather moved west from the Grand Valley area in Dufferin County in the 1920s to homestead the barren plains straddling the North Saskatchewan River. His brothers and sisters had taken up farming in and around Arthur, Ontario, a small town in Wellington County just north of Guelph. Today, many of their sons and daughters continue to farm. In fact, the single-family farm still dominates rural Ontario, and the tradition goes back to the origins of agriculture itself in the province.

In looking at the highlights of Ontario's agricultural life, and more particularly, productivity growth that new implements and technology brought, I was struck by some of the major differences as well as some intriguing similarities between farming today and agricultural life 100 years ago. Farms today are far more productive and efficiently managed than ever before. Large and sophisticated pieces of machinery, gleaming storage sheds, modern farmhouses and healthy-looking animals signal vitality—if not prosperity—practically everywhere. In the 1820s, the typical Ontario farm was a ramshackle place, where two or three log huts barely sustained a large family. The settler built his cabin of roughly hewn timbers. Winter winds, howling through chinks in the mortar, chilled the family huddled inside to the bone. The farmer possessed only what few hand implements he could buy or those given to him by the government with which to clear the forests, build a shelter and begin working the land. His nearest neighbour might be more than ten miles away, and his only livestock may have consisted of a hog or two, some chickens and perhaps a few mangy cattle or horses. For Ontario's first farm families, enduring the long bitter months of winter must have been like self-imposed exile in Siberia.

But similarities between farming then and now also exist. Today's farms are larger than they were in the 1920s and 1930s, but on average not much larger than they were in the mid-1800s. Today, farms are still worked by the farmer's family and perhaps hired help, just as they were in the mid-nineteenth century. Modern farms also possess relatively few but versatile implements and pieces of machinery. Farmers 100 years ago also needed versatility and reliability from what few machines and implements were available, because a trip into town by horse-drawn wagon to fix a broken mower could easily mean a day's lost haying time. Finally, farming still depends heavily on the weather. In fact, my research indicates that farming is still very much dominated by the seasons; hence, the title of this book.

What has really changed most on the farm is the pace of living and the rate of productivity brought on by technological change, and by breakthroughs in business and scientific practices. If you wanted to list the most important, even revolutionary developments in social life in this century, it would be difficult *not* to include the gas engine, the telephone or the arrival of electricity. These developments have likewise made a major contribution to the changing face of rural Ontario.

This book explores more than 100 years of continuing agricultural progress in the province. It chronicles (albeit briefly) the transformation of a forest wilderness into one of the richest and most agriculturally diverse areas in North America. I shall look at technological change and innovation extensively, from the early use of hand implements to today's computer-equipped combine harvesters. Constant implement and machinery improvements led inevitably to better cultivation practices. This led to higher yields per acre and per farm. Through all this, farming gradually evolved from a bitter and precarious lifestyle to today's sound business-oriented enterprise. Much of the seasonal splendour of farm life, however, remains unchanged.

Five main types of farming activity will be discussed: haying and mixed farming;

field crops (mainly corn, soybeans and wheat); vegetable and fruit cultivation; cattle and swine husbandry; and dairying. The choice of these five was based on either the number of farms currently in operation, or the number of acres under cultivation in that type of farming. This is not to play down the importance of other activities such as horse breeding or bee-keeping, but covering everything would create an unmanageably large book. Since much of farming is seasonal, I have tried to highlight those farm activities accordingly. This will seem awkward and somewhat artificial to some readers, particularly to those born or raised on a farm and aware of how overlapping seasonal work can be. In fact, the calendar is no regulator of work or leisure time, but for the uninitiated, seasonal activity does help to define the cycles of farm life.

Even as farming changes through the seasons, it has changed through the years. The mixed farming of the early decades of this century have given way to large, specialized enterprises. In the 1960s, a growing interest in rural living developed in our towns and cities. As a result, during the last fifteen years we have witnessed the rise of the part-time, or hobby farmer. At first, this new development took the form of a slow trickle of people back to the land their families may have farmed. While it has not yet become a stream, more and more people are *choosing* a rural lifestyle for themselves and their families. Farming may provide only part of their income, and these new urban immigrants may not be immediately accepted by their neighbours, but there is little doubt they are effecting a major change in the agricultural life of our rural townships and counties. What their final cultural impact on these communities will be, no one can say. More important, they are continuing a family tradition in Ontario going back decades in time.

And so *Seasons of Change* represents a journey of sorts to me, a chance to explore the world my grandfather knew and to see the world through his eyes. Despite his best efforts, his farm in Saskatchewan finally failed in the 1920s. Eventually he moved back to Ontario and never took up farming again. But when he died in 1986 at the age of ninety-nine, his memories of the farm he had worked some sixty years before were still fresh and vivid in his mind. In his final months, he couldn't seem to recall much of his city life, and even the names of loved ones had begun to fade. But he could remember as a young man feeding the horses he once owned and he could remember doing handstands high up on the barn roof in the bright, blue prairie sky.

David Densmore
August, 1987

Figure 1. Natives harvesting maize (early corn). Corn is one of North America's oldest cultivated crops, and is an important legacy left to us by Ontario's earliest native agriculturalists.

IN THE BEGINNING

The Native and French Period

A young Frenchman from Paris, Louis Hebert, has been awarded the honour of being the first non-native farmer in Canada—the first white person to live by his own hands from the produce of the soil. Hebert is said to have planted seeds at Quebec in 1617, barely eighty years after Jacques Cartier landed at the village of Hochelaga (now Montreal). Little is known about this pioneer of Canadian agriculture. Certainly he could never have imagined that he was starting a tradition that would endure for more than 370 years. In fact, he was probably more concerned with other things—such as surviving his first Canadian winter.

Still, Hebert was a relative latecomer to the Canadian agricultural scene. Various Eastern Woodland Indian tribes had been growing crops for centuries before the arrival of the first Europeans. The Huron Nation in particular, but also later the Mohawks of the Six Nations, the Petuns (or Tobacco Indians) and the Neutral Nations had all developed fairly sophisticated and systematic forms of agricultural life. They were already planting, cultivating and harvesting a primitive corn, beans, squash, pumpkins, oats, uncultivated wheat and tobacco. They consumed most of this bounty themselves and bartered the rest. Hunting and trapping were more important and time-consuming activities for the men, but we do know that women and children gathered sap and made maple syrup, collected wild rice, and grew and gathered hay crops like grass and clover. Many villages were prosperous and well laid out and Indian dwellings were large and adaptable for both agricultural and communal living purposes. By the 1790s, some of the more prosperous tribes near Detroit had even begun to acquire from settlers small herds of French cattle, a few pigs and some horses, although animal husbandry was still comparatively unknown, even among the first Europeans.

As Cartier's Quebec settlement grew during the seventeenth and eighteenth centuries, and as the growing fur trade gradually created a market for agricultural products and more arable farmland, the French population in North America

Figure 2. Log stable, ca. 1865. Pity the poor livestock that had to winter in the cold gloom of one of these early buildings. Some farmhouses then were not much better. This stable may well have begun its life as a multi-purpose barn.

12

expanded. It spilled out of Quebec into what is now eastern Ontario, and also across the border from the western forts at Detroit. The earliest Ontario settlers were originally of French descent, and they took up land and settled along both sides of the Detroit River, near Amherstburg. In fact, two of the oldest Century Farms in Ontario (farms that have been worked continuously by the same family for at least 100 years) are located in Essex County, one near Amherstburg, and the other midway between that town and the city of Windsor.

Today, it is difficult to imagine the harshness of the climate and the barriers to simple survival that greeted these early settlers. Undaunted, many of them did manage to scratch a living—if just barely—from the soil. They were the first to introduce fruit trees to the area, especially peach, plum, apple and pear, none of which were native to this country.

Figure 3.   A stump fence. These fences were made from the stumps removed from the fields. Pine stumps, in particular, made excellent fences because their resin acted as a wood preservative against rot and decay.

13

The end of the American Revolutionary War in 1783 signalled the beginning of major agricultural settlement across Ontario. Nearly 10,000 United Empire Loyalists—British, Dutch, German and Scottish Highlanders among others—flowed across the new border of Upper Canada, as Ontario was then called. This created dramatic new pressure for land and settlement, and the government of the day gave the incoming settlers land grants and other inducements to settle. More important to their future survival, they obtained their first crude implements to clear the vast forests of their new home.

Under the British Freehold System, the basic unit of land was the township, thirty-six square miles (23,000 km) in area. These rectangular townships were then divided up laterally by concession lines about 1.2 kilometres (4,000 ft) apart and again transversely every 366 metres (1,200 ft.). This produced lots of sixty to eighty hectares (150 to 200 acres), which were then numbered.

Clearing the Land

Lots were cheap in 1800—about one dollar, the same price as a gallon of whiskey—but the government's offer invariably had a catch. The settler might have to clear a percentage of his forest, build himself a permanent shelter and begin constructing some type of road before he could legally lay claim to the title of his land. He and his family would arrive on their lot, only to discover trees as dense as a tropical rainforest hemming them in on every side. Thickly growing elm, ash, cedar, pine, balsam, maple, oak, birch, poplar and hemlock gave the scene a very dark and foreboding appearance. With his crude English hand axe, a cross-cut saw, perhaps a wooden plough, a hammer, a bag of seeds and possibly an ox, the settler might well have decided that farming wasn't for him after all, and it was time to head for home.

On the still, dark airless forest floor, the settler's crude axe and lack of experience made forest clearance a task arduous beyond imagination. Axe handles broke, trees fell every which way (sometimes on top of the stunned and inexperienced axemen), and chaos rapidly ensued. It has been estimated that a man can clear only three or four acres per year with an axe. With a lot of 150 acres, one or two men alone would be helpless before the formidable majesty of the forest.

The answer? Combine forces with other settlers to clear each man's lot in turn. Thus the logging bee was born. Various types of bees became popular with settlers later—school spelling bees, quilting bees, barn-raising bees and the like—but these early lumbering bees were the first instances of the early co-operative spirit that developed among Ontario's agriculturalists. They set the tone for decades of community social gatherings to come. Not only were logging bees an effective way to clear the land, the ash produced in burning the great logs was used for making potash,

Figure 4. Early settlers clearing their land. Crude hand axes and cross-cut saws like these were no match for the dense forests of the Ontario wilderness in 1780.

15

Figure 5. The stone and stump lifter ca. 1840. Normally constructed of wooden beams and cross-poles, it probably weighed about half a ton. The stationary, tripod version shown here could rip out even the toughest tree trunks with ease. It required only one person to operate it.

16

which provided the settlers with one of their first sources of ready cash and a temporary income.

Economic and political conditions in the early 1800s aided in the rapid development of the lumbering industry in Ontario. This in turn provided a market for the products grown by the early farmers. In fact, agricultural growth would have been seriously hampered without this logging. Working in the woods or in sawmills provided a much-needed cash income during the winter to many settlers whose farms were perpetually teetering on the brink of collapse. Clearing the land thus led indirectly to the development of lumbering, which in turn aided the growth and development of the province's agricultural life.

Now that the settler had cleared part of his lot and built his crude, one-room shanty, his next task was to clear the land of the fallen bush and stones lying at or just below the soil surface. Some men planted their grain, corn or pumpkins in and around the stumps and stones because they lacked a team of oxen to haul out the obstructions. Stumps were usually left to rot in the fields until much later, when settlers cleared their fields with one of the earliest and largest contraptions ever seen in Ontario—the gigantic stump and stone puller. The stationary version of this wooden monster first appeared in the 1840s, and consisted of a tripod of thick poles, from which a heavy screw and chains dangled. The chains were wrapped

Figure 6. An old Ontario sawmill. Buildings like this one slowly fell into disuse as lumbering faded in importance in the late nineteenth century, but their ruins can still be glimpsed in isolated parts of the province.

securely around the stone or stump and the screw was turned slowly by hand, using a long pole reaching almost to the ground. Horses were later used both to turn the screw and to drag the wheeled version about the fields. This later wheeled puller consisted of a fourteen-foot-high platform, with a block and tackle suspended from cross braces. The obstruction was eventually carted away to become part of a stump or stone fence, many of which may still be seen throughout rural Ontario—lasting proof that little is ever wasted on a farm.

Drainage Work

With his cleared land now beginning to look somewhat like a cultivated field, the settler's last task before actual planting was water drainage and irrigation work. Too many early settlers, through ignorance or poverty, failed to tackle this problem. Land cleared of its tree cover, often sloping and pock-marked with depressions left by the removal of stumps and stones, collected rainwater like a sponge. The quicksand composition of waterlogged soil could be a lethal threat to any livestock unwary enough to stray into it, and planting anything but rice was impossible in those paddy fields.

The benefits of properly drained soil to the farmer are well documented, but little known to most non-farmers. The best soil for all types of agricultural crops must contain four elements: air, water, plant food and heat. Too much free water on or

Figure 7. A modern drainage tile machine. Seldom seen working on farms, these monsters can dig a trench, lay tile end to end, and cover the trench afterward, all in a single operation. Maintained properly, a tile drainage system can last a century or more.

18

near the surface of the soil prevents air from reaching the roots, slows the proper breakdown of plant food and also keeps the soil abnormally cool. Well-drained fields, however, maintain soil structure, and are better able to absorb the foraging impact of livestock and the weight of machinery. Drained soils also reduce the need for excessive cultivation, make improved pastureland and allow the farmer earlier planting dates.

Proper soil drainage, then as now, meant controlling surface runoff as well as constructing proper under-drains if necessary. Rough-hewn, hand-made wooden ploughs were used in Ontario as early as the 1780s to plough surface drain furrows back and forth across the fields. There was no set of rules that guided the settler in ploughing his drains, but this helped the water from melting snow and spring rains flow more quickly from the fields. These surface drains were relatively cheap and easy to construct. The drain bottoms could be lined with practically any non-porous material the settler could lay his hands on.

Under-drainage, on the other hand, entailed a serious expense. Special machinery and expensive tiles were needed to create proper drains three to six feet below the surface that would not clog easily or break apart during fall frosts or spring thaw. In the late 1800s, tile shaped like a cylinder was manufactured principally from clay or concrete and set end to end deep into the trench in the field. This line of pipe was then covered over with the excavated earth and an outlet was created at the edge of the field to carry off the flow. Surface water percolated downwards from the surface and entered the tiles through the small gaps between them.

Few farmers could afford under-drains until the passage of the Tile Drainage Act in 1878. This legislation finally allowed all but the poorest farmers access to the cash necessary for this vital work. Systematic farm drainage surveys were begun only in the early 1900s, by which time tile-making factories were becoming more numerous. The need for tile drains was so pressing that by 1920 Ontario possessed no fewer than 126 of the huge mechanical ditching machines needed to lay this kind of tile.

Soil structure maintained by adequate drainage is also a major factor in preventing soil erosion, either by wind or water. Erosion control practices may also include planting crops and residue cover, crop rotation, effective tillage practices, buffer strips and planting windbreaks, but soil composition may well be the key to successful erosion control. Erosion is still one of the worst problems facing farmers, and one that is constantly worsening as they work the soil intensively, decade after decade.

In the 1980s, drainage is therefore still a major concern to the farmer. Most drainage tile today consists of long plastic piping with perforations along its length, into which water can seep. Since most Ontario field drainwork was completed long ago, the main task now facing farmers is upkeep and repair, especially digging up old tiles or tubes and replacing them with modern materials.

Figure 8. "Broadcasting" seed, ca. 1820. This method of planting seeds was just as primitive as it appears. Fields were ploughed beforehand and small boys were employed to scare off birds, but most of the seeds were still wasted.

20

EARTH, AIR, FIRE AND WATER

Ploughing and Seeding

Now that the farmer had cleared, drained and prepared his land for planting, ploughing his land and seeding his crop became the chief spring tasks. The earliest settlers could only scatter their seeds by hand on the previously ploughed field. This process, called broadcasting, was the only method available to farmers until the late 1850s, and at best it was haphazard and wasteful. It usually resulted in an uneven crop difficult to cut or cultivate, and much of the seed was lost to birds or drowned in puddles. The grain, usually spring or winter wheat in the 1800s, came up haphazardly. It ripened unevenly and grew either in dense clumps, which choked off the individual seedlings, or not at all, which wasted valuable, fertile soil. All this waste added up to very low productivity.

Wooden ploughs of every imaginable shape, size and function have been the most useful farming tool for thousands of years. Their design has altered little over the centuries, and their principal function remains to break up hard ground into furrows so seeds can be planted or surface water drained. In Ontario in the mid-1800s, this often meant (for the lazy settler or those who had no stump puller) ploughing in and around stumps and stones with a team of oxen. Settlers preferred oxen to horses, which would often bolt their traces when the plough struck a stump or stone. On the other hand, oxen teams were powerful but placid plodders, stoical by nature and much less liable to panic. And being cattle, they could also be eaten if the need arose. Even teams of oxen had their drawbacks, however: when one died or was retired the other, presumably grief-stricken, would refuse to yoke with a new partner.

The oxen were strong enough for the pull, but the earliest Ontario ploughs were no match for the land. Sometimes crudely constructed by the settlers themselves, they were a motley assortment that broke frequently, needed constant attention or simply refused to budge in the hard-packed earth. Their owners quickly learned to fit them with iron shares, usually forged by a local blacksmith. Later, they added

Figure 9.   Early Ontario ploughs, ca. 1840. The plough is to the farmer what the wand is to the magician. Wooden ploughs with metal shares, like the ones seen here, are among the oldest agricultural implements in the province.

Figure 10. A modern, multi-furrow plough. Pulled by powerful tractors, these ploughs can do the work of ten horse-drawn teams—and twice as fast.

23

wooden or metal mouldboards for shaping the furrows. Well-shaped furrows were necessary for straight, efficient planting of seeds, so the crop could grow and ripen evenly and to ensure maximum use of harvest time available.

In the 1850s, better iron and steel ploughs gradually replaced the old wooden models. Manufacturers of farm implements in the United States, like McCormick and John Deere, tried to export their steel ploughs and other implements to Canada, despite the high tariff on imported machinery. In fact, the race to manufacture better ploughs and implements consumed the efforts of literally hundreds of companies in Canada and the United States, but most Ontario ploughs were made by Ontario companies. This frenzied competition eventually forced many of the companies on both sides of the border to merge, or simply to go out of business. The more successful companies, like International Harvester and Massey-Harris, went on to manufacture a huge line of farm machines and implements.

Having a decent plough and a strong team of horses or oxen was only the first step, of course. To a city dweller, ploughing a field with a team of animals may look pretty easy, but it is anything but. The nineteenth-century ploughman had to be physically powerful, mentally alert and blessed with a great deal of patience and stamina. Imagine trying alternately to guide and force more than a ton of unruly animals at your own speed in a straight line, often across rocky, unforgiving ground. This gruelling work could drain even the strongest men of energy in a matter of a few hours. And it had to be done as quickly as possible, often on the hottest spring days, since early rains could delay planting and jeopardize the farmer's timetable. In working the plough, the settler used both hands to guide the plough, and tried to control the animals by coiling their traces around his waist or neck. Only rough voice commands motivated the team to move or turn. In fact, the whole operation was very awkward, since the ploughman also had to watch the field ahead and guide the animals in as straight a line as possible.

In the 1980s, professional athletes are looked up to as models for young boys, but before the turn of the century, a good ploughman was the model for young boys and an example to other men. In 1911, the Ontario Plowmen's Association met for the first time, and among other things laid the foundation for the first annual provincial ploughing match. This event was inaugurated two years later in Toronto, in a field now occupied by the Sunnybrook Medical Centre. Some winners of these matches were even sent around Canada and to Europe to encourage the growth of other ploughmen's organizations, and to learn the skills of European ploughmen. International ploughing matches and farm machinery shows are still held every year in Ontario.

Once finished in the spring, the ploughman had to contemplate doing it all over again in the fall. This second ploughing became popular when farmers realized that

Figure 11. An early three-furrow plough, ca. 1925. Tractors and implements like this one quickly rendered the walking plough and harnessed team a thing of the past.

Figure 12. An international ploughing match, ca. 1970. For the first time in history, not a single harnessed team was entered in the 1986 competition in Ontario. High liability insurance premiums forced organizers to exclude horses from the competition.

26

ground softened by autumn rains was easy to turn over, and whatever stubble remained from the harvest could be turned under the furrows as fertilizer. Frost action over the winter helped to crumble the heavy soil into smaller, more workable clumps for better and easier spring ploughing. Early settlers believed that repeated ploughing of a field was enough to keep it fertile. Few understood how destructive to soil moisture and mineral content over-ploughing could be.

Figure 13. Transplanting seedlings by hand. Hand planting was considered the most arduous work possible on a farm, and was used mainly for planting vegetables and tubers.

Figure 14.   The single-horse, two-row planter. Like later and larger models, this planter was calibrated to drop one seed in a furrow while the roller flattened it over the seed.

28

Discing and Harrowing

From 1820 to 1880 the principal seed planted in Ontario was fall or winter wheat, usually White Flint. To prepare the furrows for planting wheat, the land had also to be disced and harrowed. Discing and harrowing the soil are techniques designed to break up the large clods of earth turned over by the plough. Discing generally reduces larger clumps into smaller, more manageable size, while harrowing smooths and levels the soil, making it ready for seeding. These operations further prepared the seedbeds and helped to hide the seed from hungry birds. Like the plough, the harrow has changed little over the centuries. The A-frame was the first harrow used in Ontario. A heavy implement, hand-made of wood with iron teeth, it was built so that the farmer could stand on it while his team dragged it up and down the field. Heavy fieldstones could be added if the soil proved too stubborn. Riding the A-frame obviously required great balance from the man straddling it.

These toothed harrows were the only ones in use in Ontario by the 1860s. The modern disc harrow, far more popular and evident on farms today than the frame harrow, did not come into general use until the turn of the century. This was probably because disc harrows were far more technologically complex and expensive to manufacture. The discs themselves had to be laboriously cast by hand from iron or steel, a process that was only in its infancy. Frame harrows, on the other hand, could be made cheaply, and the teeth easily bolted to the wooden poles.

Early Fertilizers

The importance of fertilizer, either natural manure or chemical, remained one of the biggest single oversights of farming in the nineteenth century. Even by 1880, the survey report of the Ontario Agricultural Commission listed few counties where farmers were actively using fertilizers of *any* sort. Only a small but perceptive group of farmers realized that the loss of manure value through wastage and neglect was a "natural catastrophe," a cheap and natural farm resource being squandered. Though farmers apparently knew that collecting their livestock manure could be profitable, most chose not to. We can only guess at the reasons for this. The probable answer is that it was just too much work. (The smell was likely *not* one of them, because when mechanical manure spreaders were finally invented, farmers considered them godsends.) Salt, plaster and lime were available and occasionally used on grain roots and clover, but the report clearly indicates that little beneficial research had been passed on to farmers, either by governments or agricultural bodies.

This is a far cry from today. Fertilizers can represent up to forty percent of a farm's operating costs, whether natural or chemically made. They can now be

Figure 15.   Early hoe drill, ca. 1915. This implement, used primarily for seeding furrows with grain, was also fitted with a large wooden fertilizer box, seen here running across the drill. Every few seconds as he walked, the farmer pulled down on the lever, which deposited a row of seeds plus a little fertilizer, all in one smooth action.

30

manufactured to enrich virtually any grade of soil or variety of crop. In fact, the smell of manure is probably the most typical odour associated with farming. You may not realize it, but what you are actually smelling is the nitrogen component of the manure breaking down in the air. Since manure as a fertilizer is worth much more with nitrogen, that smell may mean that the manure is actually losing value, before it is ploughed into the topsoil.

Seeding Machines

Planting seed was also a far cry from what it is now: grain seed was broadcast by hand, as noted. Root crops, like potatoes, mangels (a variety of beet) and turnips also had to be planted by hand, one seed or piece at a time. There is no reason to believe pioneer settlers enjoyed planting pieces of potatoes by hand any more than we would today. The difference is that in the early 1800s they had no choice, and so made the best of it. We can only imagine the physical toll this must have taken on every member of the family.

Seeding machines were the answer to the age-old technique of hand planting. Resisting the development of this kind of implement, however, were several factors: the farmer's natural pride in his ability to sow his crops evenly, the expense of buying an implement that could be used only a few days a year, and the roughness of the terrain. In spite of these obstacles, the first wheeled seeders proved enormously popular in Ontario. They greatly accelerated the planting process, allowing more growing time before the onset of bad weather in the fall. This in turn increased productivity. Grass boxes, as they were called, also saved many a settler's back from total ruin.

These first seeders were manufactured by enterprising companies to mechanically broadcast grass and clover, which was too expensive to be wasted by the old broadcasting method. Early models consisted either of a trough mounted on light wheels drawn by a single horse, or a box slung from a planter's shoulder so he could deposit the seeds by means of a swinging lever. The lever alternately opened and closed holes in the bottom of the trough to let one seed drop out per hole. Larger, more sophisticated seed drills came later, combining cultivating forks alongside seeding funnels. They could also be easily adapted to spread chemical fertilizers. When this equipment eventually incorporated force-feeding mechanisms and became fully calibrated and adjustable, sales really took off. By 1890, mechanical seed drills had improved so much, through trial and error by farmers and testing by manufacturers, that they had become almost as sophisticated as they are today. They have often been overlooked in studies of how agricultural productivity steadily increased in Ontario.

After planting, the final task of seeding the furrows was putting the seedlings to bed. This was done by harrowing over the furrows one last time and then rolling

Figure 16.   Drill-type seeder, ca. 1970. These large,
sophisticated seeders (or drills, as they are often called) could
also spread fertilizer, and thus were doubly useful.

32

the ground with large horse-drawn rollers to pack the seeds firmly in place. Alas, for the farmer whose work is literally never done, the next step, that of cultivating his crops, removed any thoughts of an idle summer.

Cultivation Practices

Cultivation is probably the most misunderstood and underestimated job in farming. Most people equate cultivation with weed control, and fail to see why crops cannot grow on their own if properly planted. Cultivation today does involve weed control, but it also embraces a whole range of farming activities crucial to efficient, profitable crop production. Cultivating the crop has always been the major summer chore on most Ontario farms.

Figure 17. Cultivating pumpkins with the hand hoe. With today's modern cultivators and rotary hoes, hand hoeing is now mainly the pursuit of the urban gardener. Pumpkins remain the most seasonal of all crops, although still important in the processing industry.

Figure 18.   Horse-drawn cultivator, ca. 1919. These turn-of-the-century implements did their work well. They were built to pull out weeds and lightly break up the soil before seeding, or to scuffle over (cover) the seeds after planting.

34

Every crop, be it animal or vegetable, must be cultivated properly to grow efficiently and abundantly. This has been well understood by agriculturalists since the dawn of time. For thousands of years the main cultivation tools for this work have been rakes, hoes and pronged instruments, all wielded laboriously and slowly by hand. Each plant had to be worked individually, not only to control weeds but to loosen the soil. Air, light, water and food are the principal needs of any crop, and the soil must be prepared periodically to allow these elements to reach the plants or their roots.

Unlike most other aspects of farming, cultivation practices tend to be more sporadic and unseasonal, the crop needing attention only when necessary. Since fields of wheat, potatoes, turnips or tomatoes ripened at different times—different from fruit trees, for example—cultivation might need to be done at virtually any time. Often a particular crop needed attention several times a summer, but farmers could usually fit in cultivation around other more seasonal activities, like haying. The sporadic nature of cultivation did not make it any more enjoyable, and often farm children were given the task of hoeing or weeding. This generally kept them physically active, out of trouble and where the farmer could keep a close eye on them.

Many people do not understand the difference between tilling and cultivating. Tillage refers to just about any work done in the growing process, and also encompasses cultivation techniques, which the farmer may be doing right up to harvest time. Cultivation, on the other hand, can include spreading herbicides, insecticides and fungicides as well as irrigation work, usually processes that occur after planting but before harvesting. Fruit orchards, for example, must be pruned annually when the trees are dormant, a form of cultivation that is relatively modern. Then too, the trees must be sprayed regularly throughout the growing season, the grass around the trees cut, mulched and weeded and proper fertilizer added. All this activity varies according to when the trees are planted and what condition the soil is in at any given time.

Today, mechanical discers, cultivators and rotary hoes powered by tractors have largely replaced the hand hoe as the principal implement in the field. There are many kinds of such implements used on most Ontario farms and a farmer's land is probably cultivated hundreds of times in a decade. Modern cultivation machinery may now even combine several activities in one operation. For example, machines exist which can now plough, fertilize, plant and cultivate, all in one pass over the soil. Other machines break up the soil in and around plants, adding precise amounts of liquid pesticides, fertilizers or herbicides to each seedling. The whole process is still finely controlled by the farmer, who has to decide when and where combining these activities can be productive, and when they should be done separately.

At one time, farmers felt that since tilling and cultivating were desirable practices, frequent repetition would help crops even more. This was considered the norm before the idea of minimum or reduced tillage became popular. These terms refer to the least number of times soil should be cultivated. The idea with minimum tillage is that the fewer times the soil is tilled the less prone it is to wind and water erosion. Minimum tillage greatly reduces fuel costs and wear and tear on machinery. In place of tillage, the farmer adds more chemical or natural fertilizers, and pesticides. Modern chemicals are expensive, but they do aid the crop and save the farmer a great deal of time and machinery expense.

Productivity seems to be about the same with minimum tillage, at least for some crops, but some farmers still find it difficult *not* to cultivate whenever necessary. The disadvantages of minimum tillage are that a sometimes lower yield per acre does not offset the other reduced costs, and weeds and diseases can more easily gain a foothold. The debate continues, and it is still unclear whether minimum tillage, or even no tillage will become widespread in Ontario's farmbelts.

Figure 19. Early spring-tooth harrow. Harrows like this one, that were team driven rather than ridden, were a joy to work with compared to a plough. Harrows ran lightly over the surface to break up clods of earth turned over in ploughing.

Figure 20. Modern tandem disc harrow. Today's harrows are so wide, and country roads so narrow, that these implements are now manufactured so that the two outer segments can be raised up and folded like wings on a bird.

37

Figure 21.   Harvesting fruit by the barrel. Barrels like
the ones pictured here used a pressing device to squeeze the
apples into every square inch of the barrels, which were
then sent to Montreal for export.

38

THE GARDEN OF EDEN

Fruit Cultivation

Fruit farming in Ontario has long been one of the more profitable, if risky, forms of farming, and also one extremely sensitive to changing market conditions. This type of farming has traditionally been very labour-intensive, and people who have grown up in the Niagara region have probably picked apples or pears some time in their lives. Getting paid is the job's only appeal, and climbing around in fruit trees can be hazardous to one's health. Still, hoeing potatoes or pitching hay somehow just doesn't have the same old romance to it.

Walk down any supermarket aisle today and chances are you'll find only four or five varieties of apples on display, usually McIntosh, Delicious, Golden Delicious, Spys, and perhaps Ida Red. Pears are also limited in variety, usually Bartlett, Bosc or Rocha. The same is true with peaches, grapes and plums. These few varieties of fruit are all grown in orchards that in 1981 comprised .005% of all the arable farmland in the province. This is one-half of one thousandth of one percent. Just 100 years ago, the Ontario Agricultural Commission, examining the state of agriculture in Ontario's counties, listed no fewer than eighty-four varieties of apple alone! Some of these long-forgotten varieties had peculiar and exotic-sounding names: Aesopus, Spitzenberg, *Fameuse*, the Swayzie *Pomme Grise*, King of Tomkins County (obviously the favourite in the neighbourhood), Ribston Pippin, Taylor Fish, Duchess of Oldenburg and, last but not least, Freckled Mollie. Every county in Ontario had its favourite variety. The same could be said of pears. They had names like Osband's Summer, Elliot's Early, *Souvenir du Congress, Beurre d'Anjou*, Vicar of Winkfield, and White Doyenne.

Cultivation of orchards and berry fields was somewhat unorganized and haphazard in those days. The tiny domestic market was growing slowly, and export sales were almost non-existent. Even in the four principal counties of the Niagara region, around Welland and St. Catharines, an average of less than six percent of arable farmland was under fruit trees. In the rest of the province an average of about one

Figure 22.   Orchard spraying, ca. 1890. Much like any other crop, orchards must be cared for and cultivated. A Niagara Sprayer is seen here in the back of a common farm wagon. Every dollar an apple grower spends on pest control yields an extra $3.40 in productivity.

40

percent was the norm. While it is clear that fruit trees and berry bushes of every imaginable variety did grow on farms in southern Ontario, and many in northern Ontario as well, growing fruit was looked upon basically as a pleasant pastime! It was a luxury, however, that was soon to develop into a major economic activity for the province.

Technology developed for spraying fruit trees and for marketing fruits and berries helped open markets for growers. In the last century, insects and disease were the twin plagues of anyone going into the fruit business. Local markets represented the main sales for these farmers. Many of the exotically named varieties of apples and pears unfortunately proved to be particularly susceptible to worms and flying insects. And since fruit horticulture was so recent a development, no one knew much about the value or the hazards of spraying the fruit and trees with chemical pesticides and fungicides. Pests could attack any part of the growing tree or bush, including the fruit as it ripened. Apples were particularly susceptible to infestations by the Apple-Tree Borer or Bark Louse, while peaches, with their thin, delicate skins, could offer little resistance to Yellow Disease. A way had to be found to cultivate the orchards, and to speed up picking at harvest time.

The answer was the orchard-spraying machine and mechanical picker. Experiments to study the effects of spraying fruit trees were begun as early as the 1880s and after 1900 barrel-type sprayers, the forerunners of today's sophisticated technology, became commonplace. These machines speeded up the care of orchards, but also allowed the fruit farmer more time to organize the harvest. The mechanical pickers we see today in many orchards had a rockier beginning, with many styles proving unsuitable because they damaged the fruit too severely for anything but processing.

Machines like the mechanized cherry harvester operate by literally shaking the fruit out of the trees. The cherries are caught as they fall by a soft canvas or rubber platform that looks like a large trampoline. They are then collected and conveyed to a storage bin. These harvesters can shake loose in ten seconds what one person used to take several hours to pick. Other smaller machines can shake individual limbs free of their fruit. Still others can seat two or three human pickers perched at different levels who can be extended on flexible arms right into the middle of the fruit tree. The whole contraption can be easily moved about from one tree to the next throughout the orchard. Unfortunately for the fruit farmer, it often becomes necessary to increase his acreage to justify the costs of expensive machinery like this.

One of the most recent innovations in fruit farming is the dwarf tree. These special hybrids of normal fruit trees have been bred to produce almost as much fruit as their larger, traditional parents, but may be only half as high. This has obvious advantages for the farmer: the dwarves take less time to mature, save labour costs in spraying and cultivating, and make fruit picking from the ground a breeze. More

Figure 23. A tomato harvester, ca. 1975. Mechanical harvesting is so hard on delicate crops like tomatoes that new specially bred square tomatoes are being developed to reduce this wastage. Fresh-market tomatoes must still be picked by hand, however.

and more Ontario farmers in the Niagara region are growing these new hybrids, and they will ultimately replace the traditional orchard. When this happens, the largest mechanical fruit harvesters may well become a thing of the past.

But even what we regard as traditional orchards are a far cry from their sparse and neglected ancestors of long ago: they are highly specialized and well managed, disease and insect resistant, and bear fruit well adapted to present-day needs of marketing, storage and distribution. Today's consumer wants small quantities of the freshest and cheapest fruit available; accordingly, fruit farmers have scrambled to provide more efficient methods of marketing their goods. In the 1800s customers bought huge quantities of apples because they could be used in many ways: in pies, for making apple butter, cider, jams and jellies, or for just plain eating when the mood struck.

Figure 24.   Early crop sprayer, ca. 1927. This portable spraywagon used a mounted gasoline engine to pump insecticides or herbicides over a relatively short radius. Compare it to the modern sprayer, also in this chapter.

43

Containers of fruit, especially apples, have changed dramatically in size over the decades, going from large barrels before 1900 to boxes, then smaller hampers, bushel baskets, half-bushels, six-quart baskets, and finally pint-size boxes. Today, you can even buy them by the pound or one at a time in most stores. In contrast, 100 years ago apples for shipping were squeezed into huge barrels by pressing machines that forced the fruit into every nook and cranny of the container. The individual fruits bruised easily and quickly spoiled the whole barrel, with the result that Canadian apples for export were known in Britain and the rest of Europe as being of very uneven quality.

Not unnaturally, export markets for apples and other fruits developed slowly. In the early days there was also no way to refrigerate the fruit to keep it from spoiling during long sea voyages to Europe or travel by boxcar to the United States. The long-haul market developed only after new advances in cooling technology found their way into the transportation industry, and when fruits like the Baldwin apple were bred hardier and with a thicker skin to withstand the rigours of travel. Today, heat-sensitive fruit travels by air-conditioned train, plane, truck and ship, the same as we do—and just as comfortably.

A new apparatus for producing dried apples and other fruit was also introduced in Ontario in the late 1870s. Called the Scientific, it used a wooden stove and box technique to evaporate moisture from the fruit. It was unsuccessful, and dried fruit producing has never really caught on in Ontario.

In 1870 the first fruit-canning factory in Ontario was established at Picton. After that, the canning industry grew by leaps and bounds to become the single largest user of the produce of Ontario's orchards and fields. The canning industry has declined somewhat since its heyday in the 1950s, but still represents a major market for the fruit and berry growers.

Market Gardening and Vegetables

Most city people have worked in their own gardens before, and may even have picked a few vegetables on a local farm. So they may well believe it takes little skill to grow vegetables. They would be surprised to learn that vegetable production, including market gardening, is rapidly approaching the level of agribusiness in the province today. Much of this growth is due to increasingly sophisticated methods of planting, tilling, harvesting and packaging these sometimes fragile crops. Those carrots, lettuce, beans or tomatoes we grew and picked with pride in our own gardens were but child's play compared with the scale of commercial vegetable production in Ontario.

Many counties in the province are blessed with some of the richest, most fertile vegetable-growing soils in Canada. Niagara, Essex, York, Durham and Middlesex

Figure 25. Old potato grader, ca. 1870. Barn implements like this one, in which the farmer graded his own potatoes manually and only for size, were among the first attempts to automate vegetable processing. Modern versions of this implement automatically wash, grade, weigh and bag them in a single operation.

45

counties are made up of sand and loam soils particularly well suited to vegetable growing. The muck soils of the Holland and Bradford Marsh areas and around Leamington are also the primary sites for market gardening in the province.

Ontario grows a greater percentage and variety of the country's vegetables than any other province. Just as we are an industrial and manufacturing leader, so we are also a major vegetable producer. Nearly sixty percent of Canada's vegetables are

Figure 26.   A modern crop sprayer, ca. 1980s. Giant field machines like this one can spray thousands of gallons of chemicals in just a few hours, chemicals which kill pests but leave beneficial insects unharmed.

Figure 27. A root chopper, ca. 1850. This barn guillotine was used to slice turnips and other root crops into bite-size pieces for cattle. This model was fitted with a large counterweight to make chopping easier and faster.

47

grown in Ontario, although the percentage of the province's total area devoted to vegetable growing is a tiny fraction of one percent. This huge production is also concentrated on a very small number of farms, compared to dairy or beef-cattle farming, due chiefly to the combined use of seasonal farm labour and mechanical implements.

Historically, most farmers kept a small garden on their farms. They ate what fresh vegetables they could grow in season or sold them locally, and stored the rest in root cellars for winter eating. If the farmer sold his fresh produce to a neighbour or at a roadside stand or local vegetable market, he was entitled to call himself a market gardener. In the nineteenth century, this was done on a small scale. Then the rapid growth of towns and cities after the First World War opened up new urban markets, especially for fresh vegetables. Toronto, in particular, offered a large, diverse market for vegetable producers, both for their fresh produce and for vegetables better suited for processing and canning.

The Marsh

Anyone driving north from Toronto on Highways 400 or 11 cannot possibly fail to notice the Marsh. The Marsh is actually made up of four developed marshes, the Holland, Bradford, Keswick and Colbar, and several undeveloped marsh areas. Nutrient-rich organic earth, called muck soil, makes up most of the reclaimed marshland, which produces nearly half the fresh vegetables we find in our super-markets and local grocery stores. Onions, lettuce, carrots, celery, potatoes and beans are the chief products of this area. In season, these are harvested fresh, stored in cooling facilities, and then shipped by train or truck every day to city food terminals. From there they quickly find their way onto our plates.

Anyone who visits this market-gardening centre (the other major one in Ontario is in and around Leamington) will witness a miracle of sorts. As recently as 1925 the Marsh was the home of countless frogs, ducks, snakes and muskrats, since much of it was swampland flooded annually by the Holland River. A succession of enterprising agriculturalists systematically drained, dyked up and irrigated this seven-and-a-half-mile-long by two-mile-wide area (covering 7,200 acres), and reclaimed the soil. This activity attracted the attention of European farmers in Canada—principally the Dutch—who had some experience of vegetable growing in muck soils. Later, Czechs, Germans, Hungarians and others took up much of the rest of the available land. Today, the Marsh is a fascinating microcosm of 500 European farmers using their traditional farming techniques wedded to modern Canadian practices.

The Holland Marsh area is one of the world's most heavily mechanized agricultural areas. Vegetables are highly seasonal crops and extremely sensitive to storing and

Figure 28. Modern rotary hoe (or power tiller). Normally used for vegetables and in market gardening, rotary hoes can be thought of as the poor man's plough, because they can function as either plow or cultivator. They work best on small plots of land.

Figure 29. *Seedling transplanter, ca. 1970s. With this riding implement, the seated operator simply plucks the greenhouse-grown seedlings from the tray in front and drops it through the metering cup. The bulk tank on the back of the tractor holds fertilizer or insecticide, which is automatically deposited with each seedling. The implement does the rest.*

50

shipping. The utmost speed and efficiency of harvest is required, together with the rapid movement of the produce to market. This is also true to a lesser extent in the other vegetable-growing counties of Ontario, where fruit and vegetables are shipped to canning factories and processors. There, damaged or bruised vegetables are more acceptable to the processor, whereas market gardeners must provide only perfect produce to local buyers.

Preparing the Land

The ploughing, seeding, cultivating and harvesting of vegetables in Ontario is similar to that of field crops or forage farming. In spring or fall, the fields must be ploughed first and the land tilled to the appropriate depth for the particular vegetable. As an example, in the case of tomatoes, which often start life in a greenhouse eight weeks before planting, the planting is done in May, in moist soil close to the surface. (On the other hand, celery must be planted deeply, and surface soil should be level.) Rows should be spaced apart a precise distance and plants must have enough room between them to grow easily and freely. After transplanting the seedlings, the farmer must spray and irrigate his crops as often as necessary, sometimes three or four times a season, and cultivate between the rows with rotary hoes or vegetable culti-vators. When some of the tomatoes are ripe, the fresh-market-bound produce is picked by hand, while the processor-bound produce is harvested by machines like the huge tomato harvester. These gigantic contraptions, drawn by powerful tractors of up to 250 h.p., can weigh up to four tons and cost the farmer $45,000. And while the harvester can efficiently lift, cut and separate the tomatoes from their plants, are still required farm workers to sort through the green or overripe fruits. Square-shaped tomatoes are even being bred to withstand the damage normally done by mechanical harvesting. In the case of carrots, huge harvesters can cut through the ground below the carrots, loosen the soil, pull the vegetables up by their green tops, shake them, cut off the greens and finally convey them to a truck or bin. Carrot harvesters can do three to five acres per day, replacing the work done by up to sixty labourers!

Mechanization now dominates the vegetable-growing industry much as it does other kinds of farming. Many farmers specialize in one or two types of crop and use only machinery specially designed for that vegetable. Unlike field crops, each vegetable requires different growing conditions, soil and harvesting techniques to make its production profitable. Thus, a carrot harvester would probably wreak havoc in a field of tomatoes. Additionally, the farmer may use his expensive cultivator for only three days per year, the same three days as his neighbours, and unless his neighbour's crop was late being planted, he can't even rent out his machinery. Thus, equipment costs per acre tend to be higher for vegetable growers than for other farmers.

Figure 30.   Carrot harvester, ca. 1975. Machines like this one can loosen the soil, pluck out the carrot, shake the dirt from it, cut the top off and deposit it onto a conveyor belt, all in one continuous operation.

Today, the vegetable grower may purchase or rent a bewildering variety of machines and implements to help him in every stage of his operation. Mechanical seedling transplanters, multi-row mechanical planters combined with fertilizer attachments, computer-controlled cultivators and custom-made harvesters seem to be everywhere on farms. Yet farm labour still has its place in the control of vegetable quality. Perhaps then, kids today growing up near farms still have that sense of satisfaction that comes only from working close to the soil, and from having for dinner the produce of their own hands.

Figure 31. Pulling flax by hand, ca. 1890. Native Indian labour was often employed for this arduous job. Flax produces linseed oil, a raw industrial product, and oil cake meal, a protein supplement for animals.

54

GROWING PAINS

Field Crops

The fall harvest is traditionally the climax of the farmer's year, the time of reckoning for all his planning, working and praying, when a year's labours finally bring joy or despair. Combines, tractors, trucks, farm workers and even horses are working everywhere, often long into the crisp Autumn nights. Dairy cows and beef cattle wander quietly about in the late summer pastures, paying little attention to all the fuss; the barking of farm dogs competes with the pulsing buzz of millions of insects disturbed by the great harvesters as they roar about the fields.

Ontario's field crops have undergone dramatic change during the last 100 years. Some former stars are now declining in importance, some are nearing their peak, and still others show excellent potential. Field crops provide twenty percent of farm income in the province, and consist mostly of corn, tobacco, soybeans, wheat, oats, barley, flax, rye, canola (rapeseed), mixed grains and beans. Field crops may also be known as cash crops, because their sale in the fall can still represent the greater part of a farmer's yearly cash income.

Wheat

Many Torontonians may not realize that much of Ontario's wheat is grown in counties immediately north and west of the city. Dufferin, Wellington and Grey counties, in particular, are renowned for producing high-quality, soft white winter wheat, virtually the only kind grown in the province. Unlike prairie spring wheat, which as its name implies is sown in the spring, Ontario's winter wheat is sown in the fall, and lies dormant over the winter. A unique hazard facing this particular plant is the short, premature winter thaw. If the snow cover melts and the ground thaws sufficiently, the wheat reacts as if it were spring. Up it comes, only to be killed when the temperature again plunges. But if it manages to stay put for the winter, combines take off the crop in mid-summer, usually July.

Figure 32.   Settler wielding a grain cradle, ca. 1860. It's easy to see why (statistically) Ontario wheat farmers in 1900 could feed only their families and a few others. Today's farmers on average can feed more than 100 people.

For most of the nineteenth century wheat was by far our most important single crop. It was also the world's most vital food commodity. Wheat farms dominated the agricultural scene, while many farmers also had considerable portions of their land under oats, hay and mixed grains. Most of these crops went directly into the bellies of farm animals, with only a little being sold for cash. (One major exception was rye, most of which went to Ontario's distillers.) Implement manufacturers and local dealers competed keenly with each other to provide modern, improved machinery of all sorts for grain farmers.

It's pretty difficult for a non-farmer to spot a field of growing wheat as he drives leisurely along rural backroads. Wheat is a member of the grass family, and growing wheat resembles nothing so much as a huge field of grass or an expanse of green lawn. Only when wheat is ripe does it take on its characteristic golden hue. These "green lawns," while still a valuable source of income for Ontario farmers, are a crop whose best days in this province are behind it.

Grain Threshing

Grain-harvesting technology has made spectacular progress, especially when you consider that a few farmers were still cutting grain by hand and flailing it in the barn as late as the 1860s, a method that produced fewer than eight bushels of grain per day. A major breakthrough came in 1834 in the United States when a Virginia farmer and inventor name Cyrus McCormick patented a device to cut and collect grain, the McCormick Reaper. (A clergyman named Hussey had actually brought out his own machine a year earlier, but the McCormick model proved more popular after 1840.) It was claimed that McCormick's machine could reap ten to fifteen acres per day.

The early reaping machines, eventually drawn by up to three horses, consisted primarily of wooden cutting bands that revolved like the paddlewheel of a steamboat. As the reaper moved, the revolving wheels gathered the swaths of grain, cut them just above the ground and pushed the cut crop backwards onto a metal gathering tray. A man standing behind the reaper either gathered and bound the grain, or raked the cut crop off the back for other men following to rake or gather.

At first the team of horses was driven like a plough by a man on foot, but later reapers allowed the driver to sit on the machine, saving his weary feet and allowing more working time. One successful example of these later machines was the Woods Reaper, which appeared in the 1860s. It could be adjusted for any height of crop, the rider could easily work the hinged cutter-bar and it incorporated the self-raking principle used on earlier machines.

A binder was in effect a reaper with a device attached to bring the grain to the man who bound it, and these new, improved machines came out in mid-century in both Canada and the United States. These incorporated a tying device that automatically bound the sheaves, first with wire, and later with twine.

For threshing the cut grain, only small portable threshing machines powered by animal-driven treadmills were available in the 1850s. They could thresh just small amounts of grain. But threshing was only part of the harvesting job. The grain, now removed from the stalk (which became straw), had to be winnowed, or separated from the chaff. Before fanning mills came along, this was done by opening doors at both ends of the barn, allowing a stiff breeze to pass through. The grain was scooped up by hand and dropped, allowing the breeze to blow away the

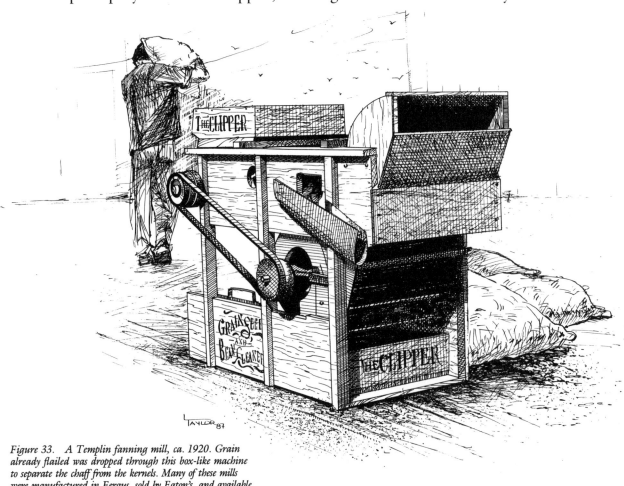

Figure 33. A Templin fanning mill, ca. 1920. Grain already flailed was dropped through this box-like machine to separate the chaff from the kernels. Many of these mills were manufactured in Fergus, sold by Eaton's, and available through the famous Eaton's Catalogue. After portable threshers came into widespread use, they were used mostly for a second cleaning of grain.

Figure 34.   Otterville flour mill, ca. 1845. Mills like this one ground Ontario's soft winter wheat into cake and pastry flour. Gristmills usually ground grain into coarser meal for animals.

Figure 35. Portable steam engine and thresher-separator. Seen here is the Climax Thresher driven by a Champion steam engine. In 1900, eighty percent of Ontario's workforce was rural based, much of it working machinery like this.

60

Kary

61

lighter chaff, while the heavier grain collected in a basket. Fanning mills were stationary, box-like structures which operated on the same principle. A crank turned a fan, causing a stream of air to pass through the box. The threshed grain was dropped through the current of air, which winnowed out the lighter chaff from the kernels and blew it out the back. The grain, being heavier, fell down through the box and was collected on screens that could be changed for different-sized grain. Fanning mills solved the problem that arose on days when the wind was not blowing through the barn.

The refinement of the tractor and portable threshing machine at the turn of the century did more to change the face of wheat harvesting than any other technological change. Huge, portable steam engines and mechanical grain separators, developed in Europe and the United States, were available to Ontario farmers in the late 1800s. In Ontario, George White & Sons was a major manufacturer of these Victorian oddities, though dozens of other firms had their own models, each touted as more advanced than the next.

Figure 36. The McCormick Reaper, ca. 1890. Cyrus McCormick's implement was the first to be widely and successfully marketed in North America. Its design was copied by many other manufacturers, and hand reaping with scythes and grain cradles disappeared practically overnight.

Figure 37.   Grain binder, ca. 1920. These cumbersome contraptions of pre-1900 vintage were the ancestors of today's combine harvesters, but without being self-propelled or nearly as productive. This one incorporated a tying device to bind the sheaves with wire or twine.

A team of horses towed the steam engine and thresher into position about twenty yards apart and close to a barn. The engine's power was transmitted to the thresher by means of long belts, which were connected through gears and pulleys to the working machinery of the thresher. Men standing beside or on the thresher fed the sheaves of grain into one end of the box, bagged the grain and forked away the straw. The process was awkward, expensive and slow—in other words, darn hard work.

As the steam engine gradually evolved, however, it also became a threat both to the farmers and to their harvest. With little warning, it could explode violently, setting fire to the barn or even killing anyone unfortunate enough to be standing nearby. These machines were also tremendously heavy and awkward to move, even after they were later geared to be self-propelling. Something smaller and less dangerous was obviously needed.

The Tractor

Small gasoline or kerosene-powered engines eventually filled this need. Still, it was not until 1905, when the Hart-Parr Company in the United States fitted one of these engines to a frame and geared it to be self-propelling, that the ancestor of the modern tractor was born. Though these first early tractors were too big and clumsy for effective field work, farmers quickly grasped the importance of the new device for all their operations. The year 1905, then, probably spelled the beginning of the end for the era of horsepower on Ontario farms.

The first Ontario-made tractors bore the stamp of Gould, Shapely & Muir in 1909, and by 1921 there were nearly 7,000 tractors of all makes in the province. The tractor changed not only harvest time, but also helped in a big way to transform farming from a hectic but pastoral lifestyle to an ongoing business concern. The Fordson, in particular, was the first of many tractors cheaply mass-produced by firms such as the Ford Motor Company, and farmers all over North America rushed to buy the new machines. Much larger acreages could now be worked with fewer men than ever before, and farms began to increase in size and in productivity. Tractor power could not only pull a wide variety of implements but could also operate virtually any other device on the farm. This was accomplished by perfecting the power take-off (P.T.O.) and power lift options. They worked by transferring power from a tractor's engine hydraulically through axles and gears to another implement. A tractor could thus run a stationary pumping engine for irrigation work as easily as it could a huge mechanical plough in the field. It could even be hooked up to the house generator to maintain electrical power in time of emergency or power failure. No wonder the agricultural world hailed the tractor as the single most important farm machine ever invented.

Figure 38. The Robert Bell Steamer, ca. 1922. Self-propelled steam engines like this one weighed so much they could barely move in a soft field, and never caught on as tractors. They were used primarily as the driving power for other machines, like the portable thresher-separator.

65

Today, tractors come in a bewildering variety of sizes, shapes and price tags. There are small, four-wheeled garden tractors, orchard tractors and even tractors specially designed to work on only one type of crop. The largest models are huge, eight-wheeled juggernauts weighing up to ten tons, with air-conditioned cabs and costing upwards of $90,000. Together with combines, tractors are truly the giants of Ontario agriculture, and with nearly 180,000 now in use, remain the backbone of modern farm operations.

Figure 39.   The Eagle, an early gasoline tractor. Built in the mid-1920s, this small tractor, and others like the Fordson, revolutionized farm productivity. They were small, durable, easy to operate—and cheap to produce.

Figure 40.   A Farmall tractor, ca. 1950. This small open tractor, manufactured by International Harvester, proved to be one of the most popular and versatile tractors ever used by Ontario farmers.

Figure 41. Modern tractor. Today's multi-speed, computer-controlled, air-conditioned vehicles are the luxury cars of the fields, and a farmer's pride and joy. They can cost upwards of $100,000.

68

Harvest Machinery

Because of its size and versatility, the threshing machine in its early form caught on in much the same way the tractor did. It was a complex piece of machinery for its day, very efficient and easily worked, but it still required up to nine men to feed and tend to it. Its major drawbacks were that it was noisy, dirty to operate and cantankerous enough to clog up or break down every few hours. With the outbreak of the First World War in 1914 and the gradual drift of farm labour to the cities, grain farmers needed a machine that one man could run easily and that could work in the field closer to the crop.

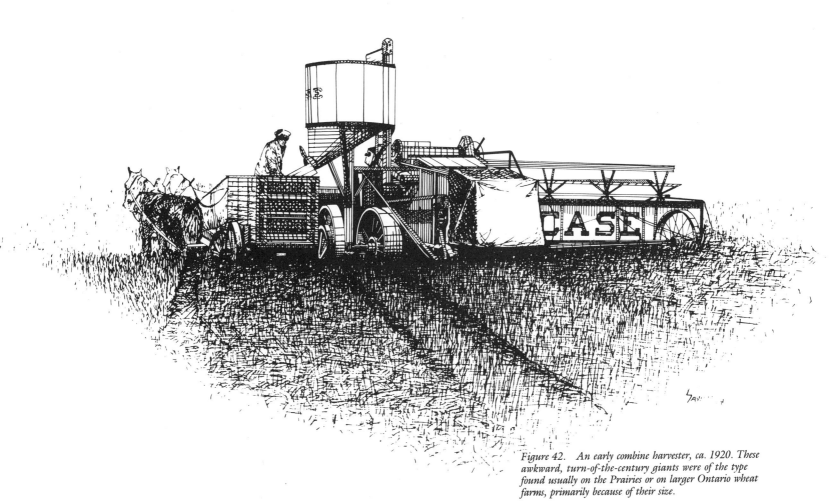

Figure 42.   An early combine harvester, ca. 1920. These awkward, turn-of-the-century giants were of the type found usually on the Prairies or on larger Ontario wheat farms, primarily because of their size.

Several decades later, the answer proved to be the self-propelled combine, really a cross between a tractor and a threshing machine. It was called a combine because various harvesting functions that before required several machines and implements were now combined in one very versatile machine. Mohammed could now go to the mountain—in this case, the wheat fields—instead of waiting for the mountain to come to him.

In the 1940s, Massey-Harris was the first major manufacturer of the self-propelled combine, but as usual, other companies were quick to bring out their own machines. Gradually, these mechanical wonders gave way to even larger combines that could be fitted with detachable devices to cut crops other than wheat. Soon, the combine took its place with the tractor as a dominant farm machine. In spite of these highly efficient and productive machines, wheat farming in Ontario and eastern Canada has tumbled in recent decades. Although wheat acreage and yields have increased steadily, wheat has been replaced by corn as the number-one cash crop.

Corn

Grain corn, used for a wide variety of livestock feed and industrial products, is a $700-million crop today, a far cry from even fifty years ago when production was negligible. Corn has been hailed as a wonder crop of the twentieth century because of its high potential to provide protein and digestible nutrients to humans and animals. Corn is also one of our most readily identifiable crops, and in the long, hot months of summer, fields of green ripening corn seem to stretch to the horizon everywhere. Most of this corn will be harvested in late fall to early winter, and sold to processors and mills, but some is kept and fed to livestock. The corn on the cob we eat or the niblets we buy in cans or packages is a separate crop from this corn, however, so anyone stealing corn from a farmer's field is actually eating cow corn.

Ontario's corn is always planted from mid-April to late May, depending on area and on the real danger of a late, killing frost. Sown with a row-crop planter, 23,000 to 26,000 plants per acre, it yields a provincial average of 100 bushels per acre. Partly because corn needs large amounts of fertilizer to grow and several costly operations to harvest, it is an expensive crop to produce. Corn storage, either shelled or on the cob, is also expensive, requiring the maintenance of a large variety of silos and implements. Huge corn combines fitted with rigid or floating headers start the work of harvesting in late summer. Powered by six-cylinder, 350-cubic-inch diesel engines, these giants can carry up to 300 bushels of corn in their bins. Some of them have three-speed transmissions, computer-controlled cutting, air-conditioned, radio-equipped cabs and options like swing-away straw choppers.

Figure 43. Self-propelled combine harvester, ca. 1952. They got their name from combining several separate field operations in one machine. They reaped, bound and stored grain, and even blew straw back out onto the soil for mulching.

71

Driving a combine can be something like working in a climate-controlled computer room.

But all this technology does not come without a price: the largest John Deere and Massey-Ferguson rigs can cost up to $135,000. Owning one can be like carrying another mortgage. These machines cut the cornstalks and convey the heavy cobs inside the machine, where they are stripped of their kernels or stored whole. The remaining stalks and other debris are ground up and blown back out onto the field, where they are eventually mulched back into the soil. The combine then unloads its cargo of shelled corn to a grain box pulled by a tractor. The loaded grain box can then be pulled to the storage area and unloaded by augers or by the force of gravity. There, the grain is stored for sale or as high-quality feed.

Figure 44. Stationary seed cleaner, ca. 1880. These machines were just glorified fanning mills. A draft of air removes weed seeds, thistles and other debris from the grain, which falls onto screens below. Seed cleaners like this one were commonly used only in commercial mills, seldom in farmers' barns.

Figure 45. Corn marker, ca. 1860. This primitive wooden instrument was used to mark out straight rows for planting corn. Corn had to be planted in a grid pattern and cultivated both along rows and between plants. The corn seed was planted where each line in the grid intersected.

Figure 46. Corn crib, ca. 1920. The slatted corn crib on posts was perhaps the only architectural legacy left to settlers by native Indian agriculturalists. Its construction allowed the corn to dry easily in storage, after which it could be fed to the livestock.

74

Soybeans

Like corn, soybeans are another major cash crop in Ontario, and they too are often hailed as a new wonder crop. In China, where they originated, soybeans were called "the meat of the fields" because of their high protein content. Soybeans are one of those crops which have yet to realize their full potential in Ontario, although they have made spectacular progress in just over fifty years. Total acreage under these beans zoomed from 7,000 in 1932 to one million in 1985.

Ontario soybean production is concentrated in southwestern Ontario, in Essex, Kent, Lambton, Elgin and Middlesex counties. New, early maturing varieties have pushed the production frontier north and east in this decade. Corn and soybeans complement each other; they require much the same equipment for seeding, cultivating and harvesting. Further, soybeans actually add nitrogen to the soil, and since corn needs a great deal of nitrogen, it makes sense to plant these two crops together in rotation. If this is done, soybeans can be harvested just before the corn crop, and little time is wasted during the crucial harvest weeks.

Tobacco

Tobacco growing in Ontario is much older than the province itself, and may well have originated with Indians more than 1,000 years ago. Commercial production of the burley type, used for pipe smoking and for chewing, began only about 1800 in Essex and Kent counties, and for almost 100 years tobacco remained a minor crop. It was not until the end of the First World War in 1918 that real demand for a new kind of tobacco began to soar. The war years brought a rapid increase in a new kind of smoking—cigarettes. This new fad had caught on with Allied troops in Europe, and when the doughboys returned home to the United States after the war, they brought this new habit and the need for a better tobacco with them. Ontario's staid old crop of burley was no match for the new demands of smoking.

A system devised in the southern United States, called flue curing, was imported into the province in the early 1920s, and Ontario's tobacco industry has never been the same. Flue-cured tobacco, called Virginia Leaf, rapidly became by far the most sought after for cigarette production. Growers plant tobacco seedlings in greenhouses in early spring, and then either pull them by hand or by mechanical puller and transplant them to the fields. Usually Holland or Cockshutt transplanters were used for this purpose, and they could plant one or two rows at a time. These machines mark the row, apply fertilizer, deposit the plant accurately and even water and cultivate, all in one operation. Pulled first by horses and later by tractors, these machines could plant up to 7,000 seedlings per acre.

The tobacco plants grew and matured over the long hot summer months typical

Figure 47.   A combine harvester cutting corn, ca. 1980.
The long, hollow metal forks at the front of the machine guide
the stalks directly into the cutting wheel, and the whole
front assembly is detachable.

Figure 48. Tobacco harvester, ca. 1960. A far cry from picking by hand, mechanization was slower to catch on for tobacco than for many other crops, mainly because only the human eye could tell which leaves on a tobacco plant were ready for picking.

*Figure 49.   The modern farm truck. It has been argued
that the invention of the gasoline engine, powering modern
farm machines like the truck, has been the greatest innovation
ever in farming.*

78

of southern Ontario, and were usually ready for harvest in August. But not all the tobacco leaves ripen at the same time. Bottom leaves ripen first and are collected (or primed) by hand or by machine first, for transport to the kilns. There, workers tie the leaves to sticks, which move up conveyor belts to be hung over long poles in the kiln. All these operations have traditionally been done by seasonal farm labour, and although wages were always higher in the tobacco fields, so was the drudgery and monotony of the work.

Curing the green leaves to a golden yellow colour takes place in the kiln, a small, barn-like structure heated by a stove or a burner. At one time, these stoves burned coal or wood, but modern kilns are now fired by oil, natural gas or even propane. The tobacco leaves are first yellowed by the heat, which may take up to forty hours. They are then dried at a precise temperature and humidity. This crucial second stage may take up to four days. Finally, the cured bright leaf tobacco is moved to a storage barn for future sale at one of the numerous auctions to be held throughout the fall and winter months.

The future looks bleak for the Ontario tobacco farmer. Trends in smoking have changed again, but now consumers' concern for their health threatens to eliminate tobacco entirely as a cash crop in the province. It is too early to tell whether or not many of these farmers will survive the transition period to growing new crops. The history of tobacco farming in the province, however, suggests that the serious farmer will be quick to adapt to new opportunities, even if they are not as lucrative. Farmers do not give up or abandon their farms without a fight, and this tradition is as strong today as ever.

Figure 50. Straw-cutter, ca. 1900. This indispensable barn machine of the 1920s was used primarily for cutting silage for animals and was powered by a small gasoline engine. Used inside the barn, the dust and noise must have been unbearable.

LOFTY AMBITIONS

Early Haying

As the gentle and warm spring days lengthen into summer, the cattle are moved into the sunshine of the pastures, and the soil begins to yield the first fruits of the previous year's labours. These long, lazy summer days signal the beginning of haying, an exciting and hectic time when man and machine are called upon to work without rest, and when the smell of new-mown hay hangs fragrantly in the air.

The word hay is a general term only, used to describe specific crops like grass, clover, alfalfa, timothy and birdsfoot trefoil, all of which are used exclusively as cattle feed. Although in summer farm animals can forage on their own in fields planted for that purpose, in winter they feed on the hay crop brought in and stored during the summer.

Haying was relatively unimportant in the early days of Ontario agriculture, because most farmers kept little livestock on their farms. A typical farmer in the 1820s might have kept a few cows, pigs and chickens and perhaps a horse or two, but his main economic concern was his wheat, oat, or barley crop. By the 1880s, however, all this was changing. Ontario agriculture was slowly moving away from this concentration on one or two field crops, mainly wheat, towards a more mixed type of farming, involving cattle, dairying, swine and poultry production. More livestock in turn required faster and more efficient ways of collecting feed for the winter. The growing urban market also required ever-greater quantities of hay as fuel for horses, at that time the mainstay of transportation.

Bringing in the hay starts in late May through June, during many of the hottest weeks of the year and often from dawn to dusk to take advantage of good weather. In the last century, particularly in the early decades, it was a hot, dusty, taxing job requiring many hands.

When the crop is high enough, obviously the first job is to cut it. A century ago this was normally done by a man wielding a scythe. This implement consisted of

Figure 51. Horse-drawn haywagon. The wagon was always carefully but deliberately overloaded to two or three times its normal capacity. This reduced the number of trips to the barn, and made driving a team of horses from high up on the stack, exhilarating.

82

Figure 52.   Early hayrake, ca. 1920. Hayrakes were used to gather the cut hay into long piles and dump them onto the field to dry, or where they could be baled.

a long, S-shaped wooden pole with handgrips at the mid-point and at one end, and a four-foot-long, curved metal blade at the other. With this device he simply pushed his way through the crop, slicing off the stalks as close to the ground as he could—trying not to slice off the feet of the man working next to him. This was extremely slow and hard work. For although the scythe was designed to be perfectly weighted, the farmer had to stop frequently to sharpen the blade, rest his aching arms or down a pint of water. Painful blisters quickly developed. The sickle was even more of a headache. A short version of the scythe, it required the farmer to grasp a handful of standing hay in his left hand while he bent over to slice through the gathered bundle with his right. Whoever invented the sickle had clearly never suffered from back pain.

The next steps were to allow the hay to dry in the sun, and then rake it into piles. In the early days, raking too was always done by hand, and a horse-drawn wagon, first used in the 1780s, carted the hay from the fields and into the barn. As an alternative, the freshly cut hay was sometimes raked into windrows (literally, rows of hay for the wind to dry) and then formed into stacks using the three-pronged pitchfork. These were then pitched up onto the hayrack or wagon, and carefully packed in so the load would not tip over on the way to the barn. There was a crying need for machinery to take most of the back-breaking labour out of this job.

Mowers

The major technological breakthrough in haying occurred in the 1850s with the invention of the mechanical mower. Like the reaper it was drawn by a team of horses, but because hay is so much thicker and denser than most field crops the mower was designed strictly as a better and faster cutting implement. The mower consisted of a riding platform attached to wheels at both ends, and it had a six-foot-long metal arm with serrated edges sticking out from one side. A blade with sharp, wide metal teeth was moved rapidly back and forth across this arm by the action of the turning wheels, and thus the expression "cutting a wide swath" was born. The level of the arm could be raised or lowered, making the mower versatile enough for both field and yard work, if necessary.

Other Implements

But if mowers meant that more hay could be cut faster, how could it be gathered more quickly and easily? Horse rakes, hayracks, and hay-and-straw-baling machines were the answer. Before these inventions came along, many hands were still required to follow the mowers.

Many of the inventors and manufacturers of farm machinery and implements have concerned themselves with combining various operations, tinkering with existing

Figure 53. *Tractor-powered mower, ca. 1950. The mower was first used to cut forage crops for animals, but those crops (with the exception of hay) are now usually ploughed under as "green manure," or fertilizer for other crops. Mowers pre-dated reapers and binders on Ontario farms but today barely resemble their mid-century ancestors.*

Figure 54.   Side-delivery rake. Hayrakes, both early and modern, were used for one thing only—to get the fresh hay ready to be stacked or baled. This version was far superior to regular rakes because it automatically left the hay in long wide rows that were easy for the balers to gather.

86

technology and adding a wrinkle or two. This often meant eliminating just one more man than was needed for the previous method. In the case of horse rakes, hayracks and baling machines, several, or even whole groups of men, were no longer needed to work in the hot fields.

The slow perfection of the horse-drawn rake made it a major labour-saving device. Worked properly, it could do the work of three or four men working with hand-held, wooden rakes. The first wooden horse rakes, built locally by their users, had been around in one form or another since the early 1800s. They were awkward, primitive implements that raked the hay, but the long wooden teeth which were supposed to scoop it up frequently buried themselves in the dirt, pitching the farmer forwards onto his face. Not an ideal situation. Later, long, curved metal tines replaced the wooden teeth, and the farmer was now perched on a riding platform above the hay instead of being sprawled in the middle of it. Daniel Massey, one of the co-founders of Canada's famous Massey-Harris (later Massey-Ferguson) Company bought the Canadian patent rights to Sharp's Self-Dumping Rake in 1875, and it became one of the firm's greatest successes.

The hayrack and wagon were also devices most farmers found appealing. The early haywagons actually consisted of two parts, a wheeled undercarriage and a detachable rack for holding the hay. Horses pulled the wagon and rack loaded with hay to a spot inside the barn directly below the haymow, or loft, or outside where hay could be raised to the level of the mow. Ropes and pulleys were lowered from the mow and attached to the hayrack, and the horses were uncoupled from the wagon and hitched to the ropes and pulleys. Horsepower then raised the loaded hayrack up to the loft where men could pitch it easily from the hanging rack into the barn. Later, the empty hayrack was lowered and the whole process was repeated.

This method of transporting and storing hay was the predominant one in use for a century or more in Ontario. Although it was efficient and saved a great deal of labour, the hayrack system still required more time and effort than the farmer could usually afford, especially if wet weather upset the haying timetable.

Hay and straw-baling machines came along at the beginning of the twentieth century, and grew out of the increasing need to ship large amounts of hay over long distances in compressed, easy-to-handle bundles. For many Ontario farmers, excess hay was considered a type of cash crop, and was therefore worth the money spent on some type of machine to market it. The earliest American-made machines in the 1850s were stationary: piles of hay had to be brought to these box-like devices and by means of horse-drawn ropes and pulleys the hay was compressed into rectangular-shaped bales weighing over 200 pounds each.

Portable baling machines for use strictly on the farm did not become popular until after tractors equipped with power take-off replaced horses. Only tractors had

87

*Figure 55.   Modern mower-conditioner, ca. 1980. This
complex implement cuts all kinds of hay and silage crops,
conditions it for better drying and piles it into windrows
for easy collection.*

88

enough power to operate these complex machines. In any event, balers were never very popular with the kids, because baled hay often replaced loose stacks. This meant there was no longer a soft landing place for swan dives from the upper floor of the barn.

Modern Haying

Haying time in the 1980s is a far cry from what it was 100 years ago. Today, one man on one tractor using sophisticated implements can do most of the haying single-handedly. Today's mower-conditioners, for example, have replaced the need to rake hay. They cut and form windrows in one operation. A reciprocating blade slices off the crop just above ground level, while a reel sweeps up the cut grass into a set of rollers. These rollers, which look like the wringers on an old washing machine, crush and crack the stems and condition them, keeping more leaves on the stems but allowing moisture to evaporate. This makes for better-quality hay and for better drying as the hay leaves the mower. Modern mowers can cut four acres per hour, a major improvement on their predecessors. Long, straight rows make drying easier and faster, and the farmer is no longer completely dependent on the summer sun to do his drying for him.

If his mower has no conditioning capacity, the farmer today can use a modern rotary hay tedder to scatter the hay for proper drying in the sun. These implements usually consist of a series of spinning metal prongs driven by the wheels as they move across the field, scattering the hay. Unlike their ancestors, today's tedders are flexible enough in their construction that they can easily follow the changing contour of the field as they move. Many varieties are also adaptable enough to be used as rakes, and their tines are adjustable for virtually any kind of forage crop.

Modern baling and handling systems have also undergone a radical change, and estimated drying times for hay have become fairly precise. Hay baling in Ontario usually produces two types of bales: large round ones weighing up to 1,200 pounds, or smaller, conventional square bales weighing up to sixty or seventy pounds. The larger bales, made by one man with the proper equipment, are suitable for cattle, but are generally inferior in feed quality. The smaller square bales require more labour, but retain their leaves better and require less expensive machinery. Quality is traded off against ease of handling in these differing operations.

Haying can be done in a field up to three times a season, with the best moisture content at baling being about fifteen percent. Under these conditions, getting the properly dried hay quickly into the barn is very important. New bale-handling systems now replace the old horse-drawn, rope and pulley system of moving large piles of hay to the mow. Power take-off on the tractor can drive inclined elevators which carry practically any size of bale on belts up to the haymow. These bale handlers are so sophisticated they can even transfer the bales from the haywagon directly onto the moving assembly.

Figure 56. Modern haybaler, ca. 1980. The square baler pictured here may soon become a thing of the past, replaced by larger round balers. The latter require fewer men to work, and round bales can be left outside for years, without significant spoilage. Square bales present too much surface to the elements and spoil quickly.

90

Horses and pitchforks at haying time are largely a thing of the past, and today's haying operations are no longer the tests of human endurance they once were. It's strange and perhaps ironic to a non-farmer to realize that some farm children today may never even have seen a pitchfork. On the other hand, today's farms can produce nearly seventeen tons of hay per acre, a far cry from 1900. This crop can represent a significant income for farmers, and for those farmers hard-pressed for cash, ignoring *any* source of income might well be a serious mistake.

*Figure 57. Cream separator, ca. 1890. Designed to separate
skim milk and cream from whole milk, these machines
were heavily geared and operated through centrifugal force.
Men were usually required to start the gears moving, but
then women or children could step in and operate it once
the whole mechanism was moving.*

92

LIQUID ASSETS

There is a general feeling among older people that "things were better in the good old days." While that may be true to some extent, it definitely does *not* characterize Ontario's dairy farms. Milk is a billion-dollar industry in the province, and dairying is the second most important farming activity, after beef cattle. The industry today is characterized by a high degree of scientific research, modern technology and sanitary farming practices. The quality of our butter, cream, milk and cheese is the highest ever, and dairy farmers are justifiably proud of the advances in productivity and quality they have achieved.

Early Dairy Farms

The dairy industry, however, was not always the model it is today. In the mid-nineteenth century, the cattle originally introduced by French settlers were a pretty sorry lot. They consisted mostly of scrub animals or slightly better grade cattle like Durhams or Devons. The scrubs in particular were thin and mangy, provided little milk and tough meat to their owners and ate more forage than they were worth. Most settlers had one or two cows on hand, but these were prone to diseases like bovine tuberculosis. Pasteurization of milk—the rapid but controlled heating and cooling of cow's milk to control bacteria—did not come along until the twentieth century, so drinking milk straight from the animal was always a calculated risk. The status of dairy cattle in the 1840s was so low in fact that they were often teamed up in harness to do the heavy hauling around the farm and in the woods.

Ontario's dairy industry really began at home, when milking the cows was often the responsibility of the farm wife or children. Collected in wooden or metal buckets, untreated milk was allowed to stand at room temperature long enough for the cream to separate and then be skimmed off. The cream was then churned in the kitchen, using a variety of wooden churns, and home-made butter was the final result. The dash churn was manually operated by a plunger, and the barrel churn turned by means of a hand crank. If the farmer was fortunate enough to have a dog, or even a sheep, he could run a treadmill churn by animal power. The trick with this machine, however, was to get the dog or sheep to walk at a steady, even pace. Since this rarely happened, the treadmill churn, for all its ingenuity, never caught on.

The quality of butter produced by the hand-operated churns of the day varied widely, depending on who was making it. Most of it was pretty poor by today's standards. Cheese factories were just beginning to appear in the 1850s, but their owners accepted only the best milk. So what few dairy products were produced were usually consumed at home, at room temperature and at your own risk. As a result, even by 1870, when a little over 1,200 tons of cheese were shipped from Woodstock and Ingersoll to Britain, dairying was still in its infancy as a major farm activity.

The Holstein

The arrival of a newcomer to the province in 1881 changed all that. If you were to ask ten people on a busy city streetcorner what has revolutionized the information industry, chances are eight of them would say the desktop computer. But ask those same ten people what technological innovation drastically changed the dairy industry in Canada, and how many would say a cow? *Not* the automatic milking machine, *not* the modern marketing board, but a cow. Not just any cow, of course, but the Holstein-Frisian, the wonder cow.

This somewhat oversized, usually black-and-white animal was brought via the United States into Ontario from stock in Holland. The Holstein quickly proved to be the greatest milk-producing cow the province had ever seen. Handled, cared for and fed wisely, a Holstein can produce from 18,000 to 30,000 pounds of milk in one year. This is far more than any other breed, and enough to fill a small swimming pool. Looked at another way, one Holstein can provide enough milk for the yearly needs of a small company of sixty people. Dairy farmers were initially astounded by this volume. Being practical men, they saw a golden business opportunity in this stately newcomer, and the Holstein quickly acquired the nickname, "the mortgage-lifter."

Today in Canada, ninety-five percent of all dairy cows are Holsteins, and the milk you drink today will probably come from one of them. There are still a few farmers who echo early critics of the Holstein and insist that Holstein milk is watery and not as suitable for cheesemaking as that of the Jersey, Guernsey or Ayrshire, for example. They claim that quantity is not necessarily quality, pointing as proof to the lower butterfat content, 3.5 percent, of Holstein milk. The Holstein's supporters argue, on the other hand, that Canada has become the largest exporter of purebred Holsteins in the world, and that this indicates quality, if of

Figure 58.   Barrel-type butter churn, ca. 1870. This wooden barrel churn was one of several popular designs. In this model, the motion of the horizontal rocking bar caused the barrel to revolve, churning the butter with very little exertion.

Figure 59.   The Holstein—"Super Cow." Milk production from the average dairy cow in Canada has increased seventy-five percent in the last twenty years and Holsteins are the biggest producers. Ontario's dairy farms average about fifty cows.

96

Figure 60.   The Durand Cow Milker, ca. 1880. This early milker was worked with a hand pump and rubber diaphragm, which created enough suction to milk the udder. Because it provides milk, butter, cheese, cream, beef and veal, the dairy cow has been called the "foster mother" of mankind.

another kind. Whatever the pros and cons of the regal Holstein, however, no one can dispute that she is Canada's pre-eminent cow, the single most valuable farm animal the province has ever seen.

Other Breeds

Of course, there are other dairy breeds in Ontario: Ayrshires, Jerseys, Guernseys, Dual Purpose Shorthorns and Brown Swiss. These breeds all have their supporters, and are always well represented at agricultural fairs and competitions. The Dual Purpose Shorthorn is so named because it can provide either milk or acceptable beef, although milk production is rapidly becoming less important in this breed. Jerseys, Guernseys and Ayrshires are smaller than Brown Swiss and Holsteins, but their milk tends to be richer in butterfat content.

The Industry

In some ways, technological change on the dairy farm has been very dramatic, while in other areas little has changed. The farmer sitting on a three-legged milking stool, milking his cows and collecting it by hand in metal buckets is definitely a thing of the past. The large cooley cans full of milk resting at the end of the farmer's lane, waiting for pickup by the local dairy have also disappeared, replaced by stainless-steel piping systems, holding tanks and bulk-milk tankers that come right to the barn door every other day. But the old ritual of getting up at four in the morning to trudge out to a cold, dark barn is still the norm for most farmers.

The cream separator, first seen on Ontario farms in the 1860s and popular by the early 1900s, began a series of changes that resulted in dairy operations moving from the farm to the factory. These improvements also began a new period of uniform quality in dairy products. The farmer or his wife no longer faced the awkward, time-consuming process of separating cream from milk, especially when results were so uneven. Now this job could be done quickly and effortlessly. Ontario's butter industry was given a much-needed boost.

Some of these changes and improvements were hastened by the growth of cities and the increasing demand for farm products of all kinds. Butter- and cheese-processing plants sprang up in Ontario in record numbers in the 1880s, and the need for high-quality farm products was crucial to these enterprises. The first factory system of cheesemaking was introduced by Harvey Farrington in 1863 in Oxford County. By 1880, there were fourteen cheese factories and three creameries in Glengarry County alone, and the number of cheese factories actually doubled in Ontario between 1883 and 1896. But the climax of this growth may well have occurred in 1892, when the biggest cheese in the world was made at Perth, Ontario. It stood six feet high, twenty-eight feet around and weighed nearly thirteen

Figure 61.   Old cheese factory, North Gower, 1895. A factory like this one produced the world's biggest cheese at Perth in 1892. It was twenty-eight feet around and weighed thirteen tons.

*Figure 62. Renfrew County creamery, ca. 1870.
Nineteenth-century creameries like this one gradually
disappeared, victims of their own over-specialization and a
declining demand for cream. Most were taken over by
large dairies.*

100

tons. When it was loaded onto a railway flatcar bound for the World's Columbian Exposition in Chicago, it was so heavy it demolished the eight-inch-thick beams of the flooring.

Implements and Machines

While the arrival of the Holstein gave birth to the modern dairy farm, another piece of technology worked the same change in the dairy farmer's routine: the automatic milking machine. The Durand Cow Milker of 1880 vintage was one of the earliest models. It operated by means of a vacuum created by cranking a handle attached to a rubber diaphragm. This was supposed to imitate the sucking motion of a calf. Obviously it did not, for the machine was a flop. As with other implements, many different kinds of machines evolved over the decades. Some were worked by hand, others driven by gasoline engine. The most modern are powered by electrical impulse. But to understand how effective these machines can be, we must first understand how a cow functions as a milk producer.

Heifers, or young cows, are not bred until they are sixteen months to two years of age, and even then they can drop only one calf per year. The pregnant cows are fed a rich diet of hay, haylage, corn, corn silage and energy supplements, to which minerals are added to maintain overall herd health. Their delicate condition demands constant care and attention. Stalls and milking parlours must be kept spotlessly clean to prevent diseases like mastitis and milk fever from infecting the teats.

For ten months of the year, these dairy cows are expectant mothers and they must be milked twice a day, with twelve hours between milkings. After the mother gives birth, the quantity of fluid produced is far more than the calf needs, and the amount is directly related to the care the mother has received during gestation.

A typical Ontario farmer owns fifty milking cows. Automatic milking machines and stainless-steel milking parlours have taken much of the hard work out of milking and significantly speeded up production. With automatic milkers, an electrical current induces a pulsating valve to create a vacuum in a claw attached to the udder. The udder is gently stimulated first by hand, then the claw is attached and the milk is rhythmically suctioned out until the udder is almost empty. When this is done, the farmer must unhook each cow, check the teats for signs of stress or infection, dry them off and then milk the rest of the herd in turn. The milking machine may be connected to a system of pipes that transport the milk to bulk tanks in the milk room, or it may be a sterilized glass bottle, easily carried to a cooling tank and emptied.

The huge, metal bulk tanks are usually found in the milk room, a space set aside by the farmer away from the cows for keeping his production records and perhaps a desk and chair. These days, this room is where you'll often find a microcomputer.

Figure 63.   Automatic milking parlour, ca. 1958. As strange as it may seem, how to tie a milking cow properly and effectively in its stall has been the subject of endless government and private farm research, mainly because of lost milking time. Today in such parlours, up to fifteen cows can be milked simultaneously, saving the farmer both time and money.

The bulk coolers not only store and cool the milk to the required temperature of two degrees celsius, but also agitate the contents automatically every five to ten minutes. This must be done because a certain percentage of butterfat globules is still suspended in the raw milk and, left alone, they will rise to the surface of the milk as cream. Homogenization, the process of dissipating these globules throughout the milk, is done later at the dairy. Hence the need for the milk to be shaken every so often. These sophisticated tanks, which can store up to 6,000 gallons, also have the capacity to wash themselves, which is done automatically every time they are emptied.

The Silo

The last, but far from the least, important piece of technology typical of dairy farms is the silo. To an outsider, silos are simple enough to understand: they have to be large enough to store as much as possible, and they have to be loaded and unloaded from time to time. In fact, silos come in many different sizes and shapes, and are far more important and complex than they appear. Silos are used primarily for storing animal feeds of different kinds and moisture contents.

The first standing structure was built in Illinois in 1873, and early versions were so badly made they would teeter over on one side or come crashing down on the barn in a high wind. Loading and unloading them was always a hazardous operation, and every year silos caused numerous deaths and injuries on farms.

Silos are deliberately constructed so that the crop stored inside can ferment and by so doing become very tasty (not to say inebriating) for animals. Heat is allowed to build up in the interior of the structure to begin the process of fermentation in the hay or grain. Silage—the stuff stored in a silo—that has fermented a little seems to be the brew preferred by most livestock, probably because of the alcohol and sugar content. When feeding the animals, the trick is to skim off just the right amount of fermented silage quickly enough so that the rest of the crop does not spoil. The ethyl alcohol that seeped out at the bottom of neglected old silos was the culprit in those farmers' tales of inebriated pigs and chickens lurching about the barnyard.

Today's silos are much cleaner, safer and environmentally sounder than ever before. Some of the high-tech ones are constructed of glass bonded to steel and are designed to limit oxygen from reaching the inside, allowing better fermentation and less oxidation. Also, many types of automatic unloading systems are now available to farmers. These machines rest in the bottom of the silo and automatically rotate around the circumference. This keeps the silage at the bottom loose so it can flow easily out of the silo and into a feed cart. A modern silo, eighteen feet around and eighty feet high, can hold up to 100 tons of corn silage.

Figure 64. Filling a corn silo, ca. 1895. Here, a gasoline engine on the right is powering a corn cutter which is being fed by several men. The chopped silage is then blown up the hollow metal tubing and into the top of the silo. Ninety-five percent of Canada's corn grows in Ontario.

104

Modern Operations

As we can see then, the modern dairy farm has all the appearance of a traditional farm on the outside, while many technological conveniences and devices are hidden on the inside. The dairy cow, for example, is still the most important single component on the farm, and she is pampered and cared for perhaps more than any other farm animal. But these same barns now contain automatic feeding systems, mechanized milkers, sophisticated collection systems, heating and ventilation controls, spotless free stalls and tie stalls, and gauges and meters of every description. Electric lighting has eliminated the dark, gloomy old cow barns of the past, while efficient, mechanized manure-removal systems have done much to improve working conditions for the farmer.

Oh yes, you can still hear the Holsteins in their stalls, lowing or bawling as the mood suits them, but their sound is increasingly being drowned out by the new hum of technology.

Maple Syrup Making

The weather in late February and early March is just beginning to give that little hint of warmth that spring is around the corner. The sun on the bright snow makes the crystals of ice glisten as the farmer heads out to check over the syrup equipment that has languished in the barn all year. Warm, bright days and freezing nights typical of these weeks provide the best conditions for the maple sap to flow, and farmers sometimes have to hurry to get their spouts, buckets or tubing in place before warmer spring weather arrives.

Making maple syrup is one of this province's oldest economic activities and has always been a lucrative part-time job for some farmers. Eighty years ago, maple syrup and maple sugar were considered important products of the farm, mainly because they were relatively cheap to produce. The sugarbush required little care or upkeep and expense, and sugaring-off time came in early spring when there wasn't much else to do anyway.

For many farmers and their families, this time was among the most enjoyable on the farm, because even the youngest children could take part. Making maple syrup was not all fun and games for everyone, however. For the man who spent twelve hours at a time in the sugar shack boiling down the seemingly bottomless evaporators full of sap, syrup making was a hot, and boring, business. It also required technical skill and the kind of patience few people today possess.

Sap flows in spring because the changing weather begins enzyme activity in the tree. This raises the pressure inside the trunk until it is higher than the atmospheric pressure outside, and the sap is literally pushed out of the tree through any hole or opening. After the spouts and buckets of the old system were in place on the trees and the sap had begun to flow, collecting it could be a sticky process. If it flowed too quickly, it would overflow the buckets; if it flowed too slowly, it could freeze solid in the bucket or spoil. (There is a lot of water in sap: wild deer have sometimes been seen drinking from the buckets.) The sap from each bucket was carried by hand to a large tub resting on an ox-drawn wooden sled. Oxen, which worked better than horses in the deep spring snow, then drew these tubs of sap from the sugarbush to the sugarhouse. There the sap was transferred to a large holding tub inside, and then via pipes to the huge evaporators. These tin evaporators were essentially large shallow pans, four feet by twelve feet, with a large wood or gas stove

Figure 65.   Maple-syrup making, ca. 1907. Almost all the elements of successful maple sugaring can be seen in this composite sketch—sugar house, vats, horse-drawn collection barrel and the sugar bush. The only things missing are the buckets.

106

underneath. The fire was stoked and sap flowed into the evaporators, the amount evenly controlled by a regulator. The sap, heated to as high as 100 degrees celsius, slowly thickened, and the water evaporated from it, rising up through special vents in the roof.

Officially it takes thirty-two gallons of maple sap to make one gallon of syrup, but the other, more important fact about maple syrup is that you can tell its sugar content by its weight per gallon. If it doesn't weigh at least eleven pounds and isn't a light amber colour, you probably haven't got the best syrup in the county. Boiling the sap properly, straining it enough times or even not letting the fire get too high or low requires skill, practice and coordination. Otherwise, you can end up with a mass of burnt, brown goo!

Two recent innovations have done much to change the face of maple syrup and sugar making. The first was the advent in the 1960s of long, hollow plastic tubes to replace collection of sap by buckets and spouts. This cheap tubing acts as a pipeline from tree to tree, with lines leading to a main tube running through the bush and downhill to the collecting tank in the sugarhouse. The advantages of this system are obvious: once hooked up, gravity does the work formerly done by people laboriously lugging around heavy buckets. The horse-drawn or tractor-pulled sled is eliminated. And the cost of equipment is cheaper per tap than the old bucket system. Once again, time and money are saved, and with the reduction in cost and increase in volume, syrup making can be more profitable.

Another and still more recent innovation has occurred inside the sugarhouse. This is the reverse osmosis machine, a unit that can be costly to purchase—up to $20,000—but which can soon pay for itself in energy savings. The traditional evaporators are run long hours by expensive fuels like oil or by wood, which is hard to come by in large enough quantities for bigger operations. The reverse osmosis system pumps sap at pressure over a membrane. This allows most of the water to pass through, but collects the sap concentrate on the input side. Like evaporators, these machines still handle 200 gallons of sap per hour, but unlike them they require only a minimal amount of energy to evaporate the water. The energy saving can be as high as eighty percent with the reverse osmosis system, and since it can operate automatically, the farmer is no longer required to be constantly watching over the whole process. Whether you use the old bucket and tap system or modern plastic tubing, the final stage in maple syrup making is always the same: clean-up time. And this is no easy task, since some farmers might own thousands of buckets and spouts or miles of plastic tubing. It's a safe bet then that whatever system is in use, when the syrup is finally in its distinctive gallon containers and wash-up time approaches, the kids will be nowhere to be seen. Some things on the farm will never change.

Figure 66. A fall fair, ca. 1900. A century ago, fall fairs were serious business. It was through these annual events that scientific livestock breeding was encouraged and really begun in earnest. They also remained important social functions and were a key part of rural life.

THE SWEET SMELL OF SUCCESS

Livestock and Poultry

The livestock and poultry industry in Ontario today consists primarily of beef cattle, hogs, chickens, turkeys and eggs. The industry supplies food to provincial, North American, and world markets, and more farmers in the province are involved in raising beef cattle than in any other type of farming. Much of this productive capacity has been brought about by the confinement production system, typified by highly mechanized and controlled animal management practices. In the last ten years, mass-production methods used by farmers have increasingly come under attack by a few urban critics, and by people unfamiliar with animal husbandry. Yet many of these practices have been developed and designed mainly to keep the animals clean, healthy and productive, and also allow farmers to work in sanitary, pleasant conditions.

Almost any livestock or poultry farmer will tell you that a healthy and contented pig, cow or chicken is a profitable pig, cow or chicken. Most of the technological improvements in livestock farming have resulted in animals that are much better off than their ancestors ever were. In fact, three terms could sum up the basic ingredients of successful livestock production today: breed, feed and disease control. Breed refers to the inherent physical qualities of a particular kind of animal; feed is the variety and nutritional qualities of food; and disease control consists of creating the best living and growing conditions for animals.

In the last century most farmers paid little attention to any of these factors, primarily because livestock were raised only to be eaten and were not considered as important as the crops. What few pigs, cattle and poultry a farmer had were fed practically anything cheap he could lay his hands on. This poor-quality feed, doled out sparingly to neglected animals of inferior stock, inevitably produced weak and sickly livestock. As a result, they grew slowly, died prematurely or produced few offspring—all of which were unprofitable for farmers. Even those farmers who wanted desperately to improve their herd quality found the cost of purchasing pure-bred animals way beyond their reach. For example, in the 1880s, a purebred shorthorn beef cow like the Hereford could cost as much as $40,000, an astronomical sum in those days and still a huge amount today. As a result, there were simply no recognized standards for meat quality. These had to wait until exporting beef became popular after the introduction of refrigerated railway cars.

By the 1920s, conditions for livestock husbandry in North America were changing. The collapse of the stock market in 1929 had a disastrous effect on farm prices and income. While farmers saw their grain prices plummet, however, they were able to fetch decent prices for their livestock, chickens and eggs. These sales helped many of them to weather the poor financial and growing conditions in Ontario in those years. Agricultural representatives and societies, and breeders' associations working through agricultural fairs, gradually made the importance of breeding better meat-producing livestock and egg-laying poultry more obvious.

As markets for wheat, barley and oats began to fade, livestock production took on a new urgency. Breeders' associations began actively seeking new breeds in Europe and the United States and they began to promote cross-breeding of animals that would produce offspring with the best characteristics of both parents. These characteristics might include best conversion rate of feed to meat, largest number of eggs laid or (in the case of bulls) docility.

Popular local breeds of cattle in the nineteenth century, like the Durham and Devon, hogs like the Berkshire, and chickens like the Barred Plymouth Rock have largely disappeared from the agricultural scene. They have given way to better meat producers like Charolais, Angus and Hereford beef cattle, Yorkshire, Landrace and Hampshire hogs, and prolific egg-layers like the White Leghorn chicken. Superior breeds and hybrids today form the backbone of modern livestock systems characterized by beef feedlots, pig farrow-to-finish enterprises and poultry operations.

Beef Cattle

Raising beef cattle today involves two types of operations: cow-calf and feedlots. A typical cow-calf operation maintains about fifty cows at a time, and the farmer grows much of their feed on his own farm property. A farmer will feed and raise cows and have them bred, a process that normally produces one beef calf per year per cow. The calf, weighing about eighty pounds at birth, is raised by its dam and then weaned at six to eight months. At this point it weighs between 400 and 600 pounds.

It is often then sold to a feedlot operator, who feeds the growing calf a rich ration that may include hay, haylage, corn silage, grain corn, oats or barley and wheat, together with vitamins and minerals. The calf can gain as much as two to three pounds of weight per day on this feedlot operation, and at fifteen to twenty months of age it is normally sold to a meat packer for slaughter. At this age the animal will

Figure 67.   White Leghorn pullet. Breeding laying or broiling chickens is a highly complex process. Pure-breds, like the Leghorn, provided the basic stock for today's super-productive birds.

Figure 68. Hereford beef cattle. Sixty percent of a steer is usable meat. Advances in artificial insemination have meant that a single Herford bull can sire as many as 50,000 calves in one year.

weigh more than 1,000 pounds, and sixty percent of its live body weight will be usable meat. Feedlot operators buy many of their young steers from Western Canada, as well as from Ontario farms.

Feedlots are much larger than cow-calf enterprises, both in the number of animals and in the size of facilities needed, and the cost of buying feed for these large herds can make up to sixty percent of total operating costs. The animals on feedlots usually spend both their summers and the worst of the winter months in large, comfortable barns.

Hog Farming

Like cattle raising, pig farming involves two separate or combined operations, both designed to increase the number of healthy piglets, or volume per unit in modern terminology.

Some type of hog farming has been carried on right from the earliest days of agriculture in the province. Hogs were considered relatively cheap and easy to care for, since many were allowed to run practically wild, and they were omnivorous, which meant they could be fed just about anything—including other pigs. They were a plentiful, year-round source of the fatty meat particularly favoured by lumbermen in the Ottawa Valley. The 300-pound Berkshire was the predominant hog of the last century, but it was never made the object of the better breeding programs that came to characterize beef and dairy cattle. Although pigs are highly intelligent animals and among the cleanest of barnyard livestock, they have always suffered from a poor public image—with everyone except their owners, that is.

Farrowing

The first operation in modern pig farming spans farrowing (giving birth) to weaning, a period of about four to six weeks. Every stage of a farrowing operation involves caring for and shielding the piglets from the dangers of the external environment. From the moment of birth, these newborns are vulnerable to a host of mortal dangers. Consider this: piglets are born with only one percent of their weight as insulating body fat, compared to sixteen percent for humans, and they can chill in a matter of minutes. Secondly, with litters as large as twelve or thirteen, several will not get enough sow's milk to survive. Thirdly, they have little or no resistance to the many bacteria and microbes already thriving in their environment. Lastly, they can even be rolled over on and accidentally crushed by their mother. Once, only a few piglets survived these dangers, a mortality rate that was considered a normal cost of farming.

New technology and farm practices in farrowing operations have made great strides in reducing the disease and death rates of young piglets. Infrared lamps and insulated

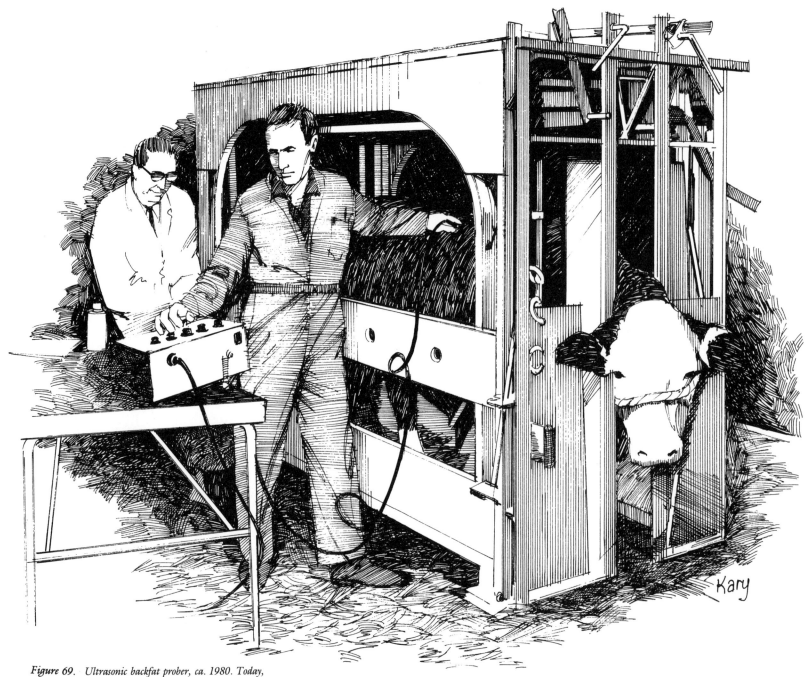

Figure 69. *Ultrasonic backfat prober, ca. 1980. Today, agriculture-related technology like that shown here is a major employer of people who would formerly have laboured directly on the farm itself. This machine is designed to measure the fat content in the muscles of steers and hogs, and operates by sound waves.*

114

metal creeps (pig cribs) keep the temperature of the sleeping piglets constant. Sows are now kept separate from the piglets in their own pens and crates, so as not to crush the newborns accidentally. Recently, automatic feeders have been introduced for those piglets unable to feed properly from their mothers. Injections of medicine and antibiotics are regularly administered, feed is kept rich in proteins and minerals, and there is always a supply of fresh water on hand. Modern ventilation systems in farrowing barns are designed to exchange stale for clean air smoothly, quietly and without producing cold drafts. Reduced stress lets healthy sows produce milk in abundance, a vital factor in successful farrowing operations.

Figure 70. An old hog barn, ca. 1845. This barn, with its distinctive roof vents but little else in the way of ventilation, must have been oppressive to work in for both man and animal. In any case, most hogs did not live long enough to enjoy accommodation like this. The one seen here was likely converted from an unused barn.

Mechanical Sows

Perhaps the most intriguing piece of machinery in pig farrowing is the mechanical sow, a fairly recent and controversial development. Many types have been developed over the years to simulate the functions of the sow, but most have failed for a variety of reasons. The most consistent reason for this failure was that their designers could not reproduce closely enough the natural functions and nursing conditions of a sow and her litter. The piglets, plainly, could not be fooled. The most recent and successful machines operate in combination with heat lamps, and are timed to coincide with the piglets' daily routine. They operate like this: piglets need warmth constantly to survive, so while the piglets are sleeping in one corner of the pen, a heat lamp is kept on to warm them. Another heat lamp over the mechanical sow or feeder in the opposite corner of the pen stays off. Other areas in the pen are designed for defecation and manure removal after feeding, or sometimes for general horseplay. At a prearranged and controlled signal, the lamp over the sleeping piglets goes out, and the one over the mechanical mother goes on. The sounds of a real sow emanate from the machine, and a row of nipples drops into place. The piglets scurry over to their "mother" for their meal, are allowed time to settle in, and suckle for a prescribed period of time. After a while, the heat lamp over "mother" automatically shuts off and the piglets gradually wander off to defecate or play until the heat lamp again goes on over the creep. The piglets then settle down in their warm sleeping corner, and the whole process is ready to begin again.

Mechanical sows may eventually find a place in most farrowing barns in Ontario, to help farmers keep alive those piglets which can never seem to get enough milk. The reasons are that mechanical sows just do not get sick, and they will not die prematurely, leaving the orphans to cope. Finally, mechanical mothers require little care or handling and do not produce an ounce of manure. Unlike warm-blooded sows, however, they absolutely refuse to mate with the boars—and their meat can be a little on the tough side! For the time being, they must remain surrogate mothers at best.

Finishing Operations

The second operation in pig farming is called finishing. This involves raising young, weaned piglets weighing forty-five pounds to a market weight of about 200 pounds. This is done largely by feeding them combinations of corn, barley, soybeans and sometimes skim milk to bring them up to market weight as quickly as possible. The quality of the feed is crucial in this type of operation. The rate of survival, growth and quality of meat all depend on the variety and amount of high-grade, nutrient-rich feed given to these weaner pigs. The old practice of feeding pigs anything available—including scraps from the garbage—has long disappeared. Today, newer, highly nutritious feeds like soybean meal, roasted soybeans and canola meal are constantly being tried, all with an eye to increasing quality and cutting costs. A combined farrow-to-finish operation has separate barns or pens for the piglets at various stages of their development.

Figure 71. Manure spreader. This modern implement literally beats manure into smaller, finer pieces for easy dispersal on the fields. Spreading manure, however, will never be a glamorous job, despite modern technology. Manure spreaders have been around since the 1890s.

117

Manure Removal

Removal of animal manure has always been one of the most offensive chores in farming. No one ever liked it, and although it was constantly being put off for every reason under the sun, farmers knew that someone eventually had to do the dirty job.

It's clear that for most nineteenth-century farmers, manure was simply a disagreeable farm byproduct to be gotten rid of as fast as possible. Few realized that the potent combination of solid and liquid manure with straw was an excellent source of nitrogen and other nutrients so vital for plant growth. Instead, this cheap, natural fertilizer was simply forked or shovelled out of the barn, often into uncovered pits. Once there, the elements could act on it in ways that would stop even the hardiest farm visitor dead in his tracks.

As mixed farming became dominant in this century, and as the number of animals on farms grew rapidly, farmers began to face a real problem. There was simply no place large enough to keep manure. More and more of them began spreading this daily bounty on their fields, aided mostly by horse-drawn wagons called manure spreaders. This implement was loaded up with the more solid waste at the barn and then driven up and down the already seeded field. A wide belt on the floor of the wagon moved the manure towards the back end, where a large auger broke it up and scattered it in a wide arc behind. Both belts and augers were driven by the turning wheels, so the early models usually left a trail of manure in the yard or on the lane as well as on the field. This could be an awkward sight when relatives arrived unexpectedly. Later, more sophisticated models were designed to handle manure with different moisture content, and the operator could also regulate the flow. Still, most farmers were tempted to race about the fields, trying to stay upwind as much as possible.

Today, most manure is only out of sight, not out of mind. In some modern dairy and hog barns, manure drops directly through grates in the concrete floor, and is then either mechanically scraped or pumped into large holding tanks under or beside the barn. These tanks may hold thousands of gallons of manure at a time and must be vented so the noxious gases and fumes that accumulate can escape. That is principally why farms may look different than they did a century ago but still smell the same, a feature of farm life that may well never change.

Market Conditions

A modern livestock operation today may involve a combination of cattle and hog raising, aided by grain or hay production. Depending on prices and market conditions, however, none of these activities alone may be profitable enough. With

Figure 72. *A modern farm trailer. Unlike the farm wagon, the trailer is used principally with the crop chopper (or forage harvester), and has two wheels instead of four. Trailers are used to transport silage from the field to the silo.*

119

Figure 73. Modern chicken barn. Chicken houses like this one are a far cry from the old wooden coops of our childhood. They can hold up to 34,000 caged laying birds, and are fully automated.

only one calf per cow per year to work with, beef producers are particularly vulnerable. Also, it is usually cheaper for most farmers to grow and store as much of their own livestock feed as possible, although falling prices for feed may make this option less economically desirable.

Recent decades have seen a change in consumer preference, first from fatty pork and beef, to meat "marbled" for better taste, to leaner cuts of both. Lately, there has been a general overall decline in the market for both beef and pork, and more interest in poultry, wildfowl and fish. These changes will make it even more difficult for livestock producers to continue a way of life to which they have become accustomed. The well-managed, efficient confinement system of livestock production will undoubtedly change as well. For now, it is a system that has long worked well for both producers and consumers in the province.

Figure 74. Spring maintenance. Pictured here is an old sugarhouse. Rough timber and clapboard sheds like these decayed rapidly in Ontario's extreme climate.

122

HOME, SWEET BARN

Barns

Anyone who has ever been in a large barn on a bright summer's day can attest to the play of breezes and sunlight that mingle in the great, airy interior. Vertical slats of light and darkness confuse the eye; dust gleams rich and golden in the moving air, and the sound of pigeons flapping or swallows darting about can be heard above the eerie stillness. The barn groans and creaks high up in the lofts, and everywhere the smells of animals mingle with those of fresh hay.

To the casual observer, barns are a much neglected and ignored part of Ontario's agricultural legacy. To the uninitiated, a barn is a barn is a barn—a place to store hay and perhaps keep a few animals. In fact, what strikes many of us as we drive along rural roads is the number of dilapidated and abandoned barns that seem to lie empty and forlorn over every hill.

While this impression is certainly valid, the picture it conjures up of farm life is not really accurate. Today's farmstead is a vital, active environment in which to work and play. Successful farmsteads exude life and activity everywhere, from the gleaming new farm machinery in the shed to the clean, well-kept yards and modern barns. Order and purpose imbue the yard's activities, especially in the summer, when the whole farm is alive with the sounds of animals and the hum of farm machinery. And it is not unusual these days to see spanking new farm machinery emerging from barns that may be 150 years old or more.

Barns have always been the most important building on the farm, and the real soul of any operation. This is not surprising. Soon after arriving on their new properties, the earliest settlers immediately set out to build a shelter for their animals. What few livestock they had with them were crucial to their survival, and needed shelter as much as they did. Rough log shanties were constructed of the timber that had just been cleared. This timber was squared on two sides, using axes and an adze. Settlers often sheltered the animals first, while the family lived under canvas or perhaps in the lee of a crude lean-to. Fifty years later, when the huge

Pennsylvania barns were being built, barn-raising bees brought neighbours together. These major social events were never held to raise a house, suggesting perhaps that barns were more important to farmers than their houses.

Barns physically dominate rural landscapes the way skyscrapers dominate an old city block. This was not always the case. In the early 1800s, British settlers had constructed small log shanties or stables whose main function was to serve as a place to thresh and store wheat, oats and other grains. Since wheat farming was the main farming enterprise for over a century, these small, single-storey English (or three-bay) barns were adequate, though dark, gloomy and poorly ventilated.

The other type of barn co-existing with the English barn at this time was the Pennsylvania bank barn. Its design was brought to Upper Canada by Dutch and German settlers, who built a larger, two-storey barn that combined storage area, stable and working space under one roof. More often than not they were built facing east to west so the yard could catch the full exposure of the sun's warmth, and they were often built lengthwise into the side of a hill. Thus, the name "bank" barn.

An influx of new immigrants in the latter half of the nineteenth century brought on changes in barn design and function. The change to a mixed farming economy was largely complete by 1875, and that meant that now livestock competed with grain storage and implements for space in the barn. A much larger barn was obviously needed. English barns were raised onto a stable, or Pennsylvania barns saw additions built to them to further increase the storage area required for fruit, vegetables and the other products of mixed farming. Barns gradually evolved into enormous cathedrals of two or three vast storeys, and went from log or stone construction to wooden clapboard outer walls with cedar studs for the frame. Hay was now also a major farm crop, and it was always stored in the upper rafters where some form of ventilation was needed to dry it. Small spaces left between the outer planks, which allowed both sunlight and air in but kept out snow and rain, did the trick. If the barn were built of fieldstones, some were simply left out of the walls at the level adjacent to the mow. These methods dried the hay or straw cheaply and required little more than good foresight to achieve.

These large barns were often a blend of Pennsylvania and English styles, some of them more than 300 feet long and perfectly designed by their builders for their functions. Farmers stored hay at the top of their barns because it could easily be dropped to the animals below. The livestock stalls at ground level allowed easy movement of the animals in and out of the barn. Barns built into the side of a hill were cool in summer and warm in winter. The thick planks of the threshing floor might also be at ground level. Below this level, or built into the hill was the root cellar, and the manure pit was usually found at the back of the barn. The force of gravity was thus of equal importance in both feeding the animals and caring

Figure 75. Cedar log barn, ca. 1850. These first primitive barns were limited in size by the length of local timber available and by their dove-tailed corners, which made additions impossible. This barn is now on the site of the Ontario Agricultural Museum in Milton.

for their hygienic needs. The hay entered the barn at the top and left through the animals at the bottom!

But even these functionally efficient, central-Ontario style barns, as huge and complex as they were, began to disappear. As agriculture became more and more specialized after the Second World War, farmers needed to change their barns again. If they could not adapt their buildings to changing needs, the latter were simply abandoned. Often it was too much work and just too expensive to renovate

Figure 76. A barn-raising bee, ca. 1930. Events like this one became the cornerstone of rural life in Ontario. Often as many as 200 men and nearly as many women from the community would show up. By 1950, manpower was so scarce that only Mennonite communities could successfully raise barns this way.

126

stables and pens for ever-larger herds of cattle, sheep or pigs. And with the advent of new hay-baling and handling machinery, hay no longer required as much storage space. As a result, the older barns today in the Ontario countryside are almost always examples or adaptations of these Pennsylvania-style giants. Often additions of a later date jut out at different angles and may be constructed of different materials entirely.

Figure 77.   A modified bank barn. Barns were frequently added to, rather than torn down and rebuilt. The barn pictured here might well have started its life as a single building, with the additions, separate storeys and silos all added piecemeal over the decades. No two barns are ever alike.

127

Modern dairy farms, on the other hand, often consist of a series of large and small barns, the large one for milking, the smaller ones for heifers, calves or non-lactating cows. Poultry and pig barns are electronically controlled and monitored for proper heating, lighting and ventilation. These greenhouse conditions are regulated automatically at all times to provide livestock and poultry with the best possible growing conditions. Modern barns like this, which can hold as many as 10,000 broiler chickens or layers, are sometimes criticized because they provide artificial, unnatural conditions. Critics should remember, however, that mass production techniques available to farmers have made a major contribution to the marketing of inexpensive, high-quality food.

Farmhouses

If the farmhouse took second place to the barn as the centre of work, it had its own cherished place as the heart of the farmstead and the centre of social life in the community. It is often difficult for city people to understand the attraction of many of the old farmhouses that dot the countryside. For many of us, changing houses is a routine part of our lifestyle, an expensive and upsetting habit which we treat as normal. For the farmer, however, keeping a home as part of his business, or as an ongoing way of life that will accommodate his children and grandchildren, is normal.

We have already looked at the evolution of the Ontario farmhouse from its earliest beginnings as a primitive, one-room dwelling better fit for animals. This phase did not last long in the province, for two reasons. First, the climate was so severe that good accommodation, carefully constructed with an eye to extremes of weather, was absolutely necessary. Second, many of the earliest United Empire Loyalists brought with them from the eastern United States the familiar building styles and construction skills of their previous homes. The first crude huts hacked from the surrounding forests were, in most cases, never meant to be more than temporary shelters. When the settler had accumulated enough extra capital to buy local construction materials, he could begin to plan and build a proper house for himself and his growing family.

Local materials, such as limestone, bricks, lumber and fieldstones provided the impetus for change. These first neo-classical Loyalist homes were invariably of one or one-and-a-half storeys, with steep-pitched roofs, few windows and little decorative trim. At first it was preferable to build fewer than two storeys, since the owner was taxed on the number of floors in his house. The half-storey that resulted from this Canadian compromise was frequently more like a cramped attic, stiflingly hot in summer and frigid in winter. Hallways were narrow in these houses, the rooms tiny, and there was little insulation anywhere. As bad as these early dwellings were,

Figure 78. A country store, ca. 1900. In stores like these at the turn of the century eggs sold for eight cents a dozen and steak for ten cents a pound. In those days, store owners were required to give credit to their customers in bad times or risk losing them in good times.

129

Figure 79.   Pumping windmill, ca. 1930. These mechanical implements were used as a source of energy for everything from pumping water to driving stationary barn implements. With the advent of electricity and small gasoline engines, they became relics, symbols of a bygone era.

130

however, they were a major improvement over log shanties, and by 1880 nearly half the houses in Ontario were constructed of stone, brick or frame. This was considered first-class housing at the time, and still is.

Gradually these small, tidy, rather spare little homes gave way to larger, two-storey dwellings that contained as many as six bedrooms. Farms were getting progressively larger in size, requiring more workers, so the average farm family grew enough boys to help out. This meant many more bedrooms and a much larger kitchen than ever before. In fact, what strikes the casual visitor the most about farmhouses, old and new, is the size of the kitchen. It's always huge—at least compared to the other rooms in the house. If the house was the soul of the farm, the kitchen was the soul of the house. Farmers ate, talked, rested, drank and even watched TV in their kitchens and thanks to the microwave oven, this tradition will likely continue.

These houses grew in other ways too: often unheated summer kitchens, separate laundries, smoke-houses or woodsheds were added on. This was necessary because successive generations required different functions from their rooms, and also

Figure 80. Fieldstone farmhouse, ca. 1880. Early Ontario building materials included large rocks and stones free for the taking, and which were stronger and more durable than wood. Almost all fieldstone farmhouses were built before 1900.

131

*Figure 81.   Carriage and blacksmith shop, ca. 1875. If
the general store provided the casual meeting-place for
the town's women folk, the blacksmith's shop filled the same
function for the men.*

132

because as farmers became prosperous, they wanted their houses to reflect their new status. Architectural integrity invariably gave way to practical needs, however, since the owner often wore the hat of builder and designer at the same time. A two-storey frame house with eight rooms could cost between $2,700 and $3,000 in the 1840s. There is no estimate available for the additional cost of the two-holer out back.

Farmhouses today seem to follow no pattern of style or design, at least not a recognizable one. Many original architectural features have been eliminated, added to or just plain covered up. While it is not rare to find a farmhouse more than a century old, it is rare to find one in its original state. Farmers always seemed to be tinkering with their machinery, and they carried over this habit into additions on their houses. In fact, it is common today to see farmhouses and outbuildings made up entirely of different materials, with little thought given to what the proper dimensions might be. For farmers, a house was a place to rest between workdays, and many a farm wife over the generations has lamented that her man seemed to prefer the company of the barn to that of the house.

Figure 82. An old implement dealership, ca. 1920. Good credit and service from a local dealer was crucial to all farmers, especially when things went wrong at harvest time.

Figure 83. A modern Co-op outlet, ca. 1985. The distinctive logo on this building is a symbol, representing nearly seventy-five years of wholesale and retail service to the farming community. Everything from implements to seed grain and home hardware can be found in many of these stores. They are owned and operated through the United Co-operatives of Ontario.

134

FARM FUTURES

In the era of test-tube babies, Star Wars, microchips and robotic labour, traditional farming is being served by an ever-increasing flow of research and development. As we have seen from the preceding chapters, the applications of science and technology on the farm have worked wonders in transforming farming from a pastoral way of life to a family business. Farmers today are better educated, have more access to the latest technology and can cope with more of the variables in farming than ever before. Where is agriculture going, you may ask? Where it has always gone—forward.

Breeding

Perhaps nowhere are these improved conditions better illustrated than in new breeding practices for both plants and animals. From the origins of agriculture in the province until the 1920s, knowledge of breeding practices grew only very slowly. The old rural practice of leading the family bull or boar down country roads to service a neighbour's cows or pigs was good enough for most farmers. This slow growth in expertise was not helped by purebred animals.

Governments, farmers' associations and individuals made sporadic attempts to introduce newer breeds. It was only in the 1920s, however, that these efforts began to be applied systematically and with wide effect. New strains of wheat and cereal crops were pioneered at the Ontario Agricultural College in Guelph, and corn hybrids were developed to meet the ever-changing conditions of soil and climate. As genetics and gene splicing introduced newer, hardier, more disease-resistant varieties of crops, so research on artificial insemination brought revolutionary changes in the dairy and beef-cattle industries.

As we have already seen, much of the livestock in early Ontario was unsuitable for successful farming. New breeds of cattle, like the Devons and Durhams, the Holsteins and the Charolais and Angus have done much to change this. Yet even

Figure 84. A modern milk room, ca. 1987. Increasingly, progressive farmers are turning to the microcomputer to help them with a whole range of management problems and decisions. Computers are particularly useful for measuring the productivity of dairy cows, seen here.

136

these admittedly excellent breeds of milk- and meat-producing cattle had one major drawback for serious producers—getting the best bulls and cows together at optimum mating times.

Enter artificial insemination in the 1940s. In this technique, semen from high-quality bulls can be obtained in special facilities, frozen in vials, sold to farmers and then inserted in cows when they are in heat. Bulls and cows no longer had to live in the same neighbourhood to get together, and since bulls made poor fathers anyway, no one was the wiser. Frozen semen can be far more easily and cheaply stored and transported than can the bull itself, and this protein can be potent for up to twenty years. With this technique it is even possible for bulls to sire calves long after the bulls have died of old age. A.I., as it is known, has proven so successful in just forty years that nearly all dairy and many beef cattle bred in Ontario are artificially inseminated. Today, a vial of bull semen from a top purebred Charolais or Holstein can cost as much as $1,000, and semen is an important and growing international export.

Embryo transfer is the female equivalent of artificial insemination. Cows are fed special hormones to encourage the growth of a larger number of eggs than would normally be the case, and they are then bred by artificial insemination. The resulting eight to ten embryos are first nurtured and then flushed from the cow's uterus. Finally, the embryos are transplanted into a number of other cows in heat, thus greatly increasing the number of calves born to one set of parents. Commercial application of this process has just begun.

Aiding the farmer and breeder in these two processes are small heat-detection devices that, when placed near the female's uterus, can determine when that animal is ovulating, and therefore when it should be sired. Timing is crucial to breeders, because a missed pregnancy is a lost opportunity and possibly a serious financial blow. Much of the guesswork has been systematically eliminated from the whole breeding cycle, and as a result, livestock are more healthy and productive than ever before.

Scientific breeding practices have not only drastically increased the number of animals on Ontario farms, they are also indirectly responsible for improved quality. Related agricultural research, centred on finding newer, cheaper, more nutritious feeds for livestock has greatly aided the breeding of sturdy animals. Plants are cross-bred for a combination of better nutrient and moisture content, and for survivability, both indispensable qualities of good feed. Thus, animals, farmers and consumers all benefit from better feed conversion, the process whereby food intake is converted either to milk or to muscle.

Breeding can accomplish other tremendous gains for farmers. In the case of pigs, Yorkshire sows have a good reputation for farrowing more and heavier piglets than

Figure 85. Biotechnology and research, centering on such processes as nitrogen fixation in plants, are now major and accepted parts of modern agriculture. Almost as much research in agriculture is now carried out in laboratories as in the fields.

other breeds. Hampshire boars are renowned as aggressive sires. Putting the two together maximizes the best qualities of both breeds, in this case producing large litters with many aggressive male boars.

In the case of beef cattle, much research is currently being done on the best size and weight at which to sell slaughter cattle. Many scientists and farmers believe that the bigger a calf is at birth, the sooner it can reach market weight. In these questions, feed conversion rates versus prices of feed tend to be dominant issues. Evidence does seem to indicate that bigger breeds of cattle convert feed faster to muscle than do smaller breeds. In this case, big definitely is beautiful.

The science of developing poultry hybrids is now one of the most complex in modern farming. The confinement system, with its optimum growing and laying conditions, is designed to bring birds to market weight as fast and cheaply as possible or to make them lay large numbers of eggs. This demands a different kind of bird. Accordingly, new breeds have been carefully and specifically developed to cope with the conditions of artificial confinement systems.

Every minute of a broiler's or layer's life is now strictly controlled by the producer. For example, broilers and roasters are bred especially so that they can most efficiently and cheaply convert feed to meat, just like the best beef cattle. They have a feed-conversion ratio of exactly 1.93 pounds of feed to one pound of meat gained, and can be ready for market in an astonishing *seven weeks* from birth. Developments like these are the result of decades of work on hybrid animals, with the added benefit that many have proven to be more disease-resistant than their ancestors.

Egg-laying hybrids like the Leghorn, New Hampshire, Light Sussex and White ` Plymouth Rock have been bred to lay eggs with thicker shells to prevent easy breakage. In addition, the constant artificial daylight of many egg-laying operations has meant that a single hen can now lay as many as 260 eggs a year. Fifty years ago, a normal free-range hen could lay about seventy-five. Even their cages have been designed with sloped bottoms so that the eggs can roll down for easy, automated removal.

Figure 86. Modern computer-aided belt feeder, seen with operator. Automated feeding systems like this one have eliminated most of the guesswork and much of the back-breaking labour from the daily feeding of livestock. The control panel on the left would always be inside the barn.

Conclusion

From about 1920 on, the pace and productivity of agricultural life in the province have been steadily increasing. The introduction of the diesel-engine tractor, the combine harvester, electricity and the telephone changed the nature of farming practically overnight. An uncertain labour supply brought about by urbanization and two world wars made advanced, labour-saving machines and practices vital to all farmers. The food-processing industry grew by leaps and bounds in that period, taking an increasing role in sponsoring agricultural research. The benefits of sustained soil productivity, decade after decade, were constantly being weighed against the need for intensive agriculture. As farms grew larger and more specialized, costs escalated accordingly, and farmers were constantly searching for ways to cut those costs and at the same time be more efficient.

New machinery and technology, despite its potential for savings in labour, has sometimes been a double-edged sword. The operating and fuel costs of a large combine, tractor and assorted hydraulic implements, added to the constant need for top-quality but expensive feeds and fertilizers, can represent the largest parts of any farmer's operating costs. Better machinery can mean increased productivity per acre or per animal, even though these savings may be offset by falling prices or cost increases elsewhere. Gradually, the debt load carried by farmers can increase to a critical point.

But newer devices, techniques and materials are on the way to help farmers cope with the increasing cost of farming. New fuels like vegetable oils and alcohol to drive tractors and implements are constantly being tested. Methane-making machines that use common farmyard manure as a raw material may eventually prove to be a major electricity producer. Heat exchangers are already widely used in dairy operations to conserve the heat lost in cooling milk, using it instead to heat wash water. Solar heating could complement electricity in heating the barns of the future. Even the microcomputer is finding its place on more and more farms, aiding the modern farmer in everything from field analysis to accounting practices.

At the turn of the century, one farmer could feed only five other people. In 1987, one farmer could feed himself and 100 others as well. This dramatic increase in productivity has not been a cure-all for most farmers, but it has undoubtedly kept many in business. Farming, like most businesses, is still subject to changing economic, social and environmental conditions that can cripple any operation.

By the 1980s, nearly one-half of Ontario's farmers needed off-farm income to survive. Many had sold off or rented most of their land in the hope of returning to full-time farming when and if conditions improved. But part-time and hobby farmers, many of them born and raised in cities, had moved in to fill this gap. Old problems like pest and disease control, uncertain weather conditions and a dwindling labour supply have largely been eliminated as factors in farming. In their

Figure 87.   Hybrid corn research, ca. 1987. Plant genetic engineers can now grow healthy plants from cells instead of seeds, and hydroponic plants which require neither soil nor fields in which to grow.

143

place, however, have come new problems and challenges, such as debt management, fluctuating land and commodity prices, and a lack of commitment by the government to preserving foodlands. Farming remains as precarious as ever, even as the face of agriculture constantly changes. Only time will tell if technology alone will save the farm as a viable family operation.

Mass-production techniques and the new agribusiness have forced farmers to adopt practices many find objectionable. Some have said that once machines dominate

Figure 88. A modern farmstead, ca. 1980s. All the elements of a modern farm operation can be seen in this panoramic sketch. Something of the past, present and future of buildings and implements may be found on just about any farm in the province.

144

their farm day, the only choice left to them is to become mechanics or to leave farming altogether. Still others feel forced to acquire more land, more chemicals and more debt to compete with their neighbours. And most would still rather spend every working day on the farm, instead of in a factory or brickyard. Those who stay will continue to confront the problems and opportunities that will always go with farming. The world will always need farmers, and farmers will always need their land.

List of Illustrations

Front Cover: Early horse drawn plow. (Louise Taylor)
Title Page: Old Barn and Corn Crib. (George Rickard)

In the beginning . . .
1. Natives harvesting maize (early corn). (Louise Taylor)
2. Log stable, ca. 1865. (George Rickard)
3. A stump fence. (Kary Suronen)
4. Early settlers clearing their land. (Kary Suronen)
5. The stone and stump lifter, ca. 1840. (Kary Suronen)
6. An old Ontario sawmill. (George Rickard)
7. A modern drainage tile machine. (Kary Suronen)

Earth, air, fire and water
8. "Broadcasting" seed, ca. 1820. (Martha Robinson)
9. Early Ontario ploughs, ca. 1840. (Martha Robinson)
10. A modern, multi-furrow plough. (Kary Suronen)
11. An early three-furrow plough, ca. 1925. (Louise Taylor)
12. An international ploughing match, ca. 1970. (Louise Taylor)
13. Transplanting seedlings by hand. (Louise Taylor)
14. The single-horse, two-row planter. (Martha Robinson)
15. Early hoe drill, ca. 1915. (Louise Taylor)
16. Drill-type seeder, ca. 1970. (Kary Suronen)
17. Cultivating pumpkins with the hand hoe. (Kary Suronen)
18. Horse-drawn cultivator, ca. 1919. (Louise Taylor)
19. Early spring-tooth harrow. (Louise Taylor)
20. Modern tandem disc harrow. (Kary Suronen)

The garden of Eden
21. Harvesting fruit by the barrel. (Louise Taylor)
22. Orchard spraying, ca. 1890. (Kary Suronen)
23. A tomato harvester, ca. 1975. (Kary Suronen)
24. Early crop sprayer, ca. 1927. (Kary Suronen)
25. Old potato grader, ca. 1870. (Louise Taylor)
26. A modern crop sprayer, ca. 1980s. (Kary Suronen)
27. A root chopper, ca. 1850. (Louise Taylor)
28. Modern rotary hoe (or power tiller). (Kary Suronen)
29. Seedling transplanter, ca. 1970s. (Kary Suronen)
30. Carrot harvester, ca. 1975. (Kary Suronen)

Growing pains
31. Pulling flax by hand, ca. 1890. (Martha Robinson)
32. Settler wielding a grain cradle, ca. 1860. (Louise Taylor)
33. A Templin fanning mill, ca. 1920. (Louise Taylor)
34. Otterville flour mill, ca. 1845. (George Rickard)
35. Portable steam engine and thresher-separator. (Kary Suronen)
36. The McCormick Reaper, ca. 1890. (Louise Taylor)
37. Grain binder, ca. 1920. (Kary Suronen)
38. The Robert Bell Steamer, ca. 1922. (George Rickard)
39. The Eagle, an early gasoline tractor. (George Rickard)
40. A Farmall tractor, ca. 1950. (Kary Suronen)
41. Modern tractor. (Kary Suronen)
42. An early combine harvester, ca. 1920. (Louise Taylor)
43. Self-propelled combine harvester, ca. 1952. (Louise Taylor)
44. Stationary seed cleaner, ca. 1880. (Louise Taylor)

45. Corn marker, ca. 1860. (Louise Taylor)
46. Corn crib, ca. 1920. (Kary Suronen)
47. Combine harvester cutting corn, ca. 1980. (Louise Taylor)
48. Tobacco harvester, ca. 1960. (Martha Robinson)
49. The modern farm truck. (Kary Suronen)

Lofty ambitions
50. Straw-cutter, ca. 1900. (Kary Suronen)
51. Horse-drawn haywagon. (Martha Robinson)
52. Early hayrake, ca. 1920. (Louise Taylor)
53. Tractor-powered mower, ca. 1950. (Kary Suronen)
54. Side-delivery rake. (Louise Taylor)
55. Modern mower-conditioner, ca. 1980. (Kary Suronen)
56. Modern haybaler. (Kary Suronen)

Liquid assets
57. Cream separator, ca. 1980. (Louise Taylor)
58. Barrel-type butter churn, ca. 1870. (Martha Robinson)
59. The Holstein—"Super Cow". (Louise Taylor)
60. The Durand Cow Milker, ca. 1880. (Kary Suronen)
61. Old cheese factory, North Gower, 1895. (Kary Suronen)
62. Renfrew County creamery, ca. 1870. (Louise Taylor)
63. Automatic milking parlour, ca. 1960. (Kary Suronen)
64. Filling a corn silo, ca. 1895. (Louise Taylor)
65. Maple-syrup making, ca. 1907. (Louise Taylor)

The sweet smell of success
66. A fall fair, ca. 1900. (Martha Robinson)
67. White Leghorn pullet. (Martha Robinson)
68. Hereford beef cattle. (Kary Suronen)
69. Ultrasonic backfat prober, ca. 1980. (Kary Suronen)
70. An old hog barn, ca. 1845. (George Rickard)
71. Manure spreader. (Kary Suronen)
72. A modern farm trailer. (Kary Suronen)
73. Modern chicken barn. (Kary Suronen)

Home, sweet barn
74. Spring maintenance. (George Rickard)
75. Cedar log barn, ca. 1850. (George Rickard)
76. A barn-raising bee, ca. 1930. (Kary Suronen)
77. A modified bank barn. (Kary Suronen)
78. A country store, ca. 1900. (George Rickard)
79. Pumping windmill, ca. 1930. (Kary Suronen)
80. Fieldstone farmhouse, ca. 1880. (Louise Taylor)
81. Carriage and blacksmith shop, ca. 1875. (George Rickard)
82. An old implement dealership, ca. 1920. (George Rickard)

Farm futures?
83. A modern Co-op outlet, ca. 1985. (Louise Taylor)
84. A modern milk room, ca. 1987. (Kary Suronen)
85. Biotechnology and research. (Kary Suronen)
86. A modern computer-aided belt feeder. (Kary Suronen)
87. Hybrid corn research. (Kary Suronen)
88. Modern farmstead, ca. 1980s. (Kary Suronen)

List of References

Primary Sources
Ontario Archives, Toronto. Photographic Collection, Library files.
Ontario Agricultural Museum, Milton. Library files.
Ontario Ministry of Agriculture and Food. Photographic Services Division,
   University of Guelph. Reuben Sallows photographic collection.

Journals
Farmers Advocate. Various issues.
Canadian Farmer. Various issues.
Farm and Country. Various issues.

Secondary Sources
Agriculture and Food, Ontario Ministry of. Assorted *Factsheets*.

————. Agricultural Representatives Branch, and University of Guelph.
   Ontario Farm Management Analysis Project, 1985. Guelph, 1986.

Agriculture, Dep't. of. Bulletin #1: "Maple Sugar and Syrup." Ottawa,
   1906.

Agriculture, United States Dep't. of. "Soybeans as Human Food."
   Utilization Research Report, No. 5. Washington, 1979.

Ardrey, Robert L. *American Agricultural Implements*. Reprint New York:
   Arno Press, 1972. © 1984 by the author.

Arthur, Eric and Witney, Dudley. *The Barn: A Vanishing Landmark in
   North America*. Toronto: McClelland and Stewart, 1972.

Blake, V.B. and Greenhill, Ralph. *Rural Ontario*. Toronto: University of
   Toronto Press, 1969.

Culpin, Claude. *Farm Machinery*. 9th ed. Granada Publishing, 1976.

Fellows, Myrtie. *Maple-Sugaring: The Way We Do It*. Battleboro, Vermont:
   Stephen Greene Press, 1972.

Fisher, G.A. "The Economics of Soybean Production in Ontario, 1980."
   (Pamphlet) Toronto: Economics Branch, Ontario Ministry of Agriculture
   and Food, 1981.

Food and Agriculture, Ministry of. "Agricultural Statistics for Ontario,
   1941–1978." Toronto, 1979.

————. "The Soybean Industry in Ontario." Toronto: Economics Branch,
   1972.

Fuller, Tony. "The Development of Farming and Farm Life in Ontario."
   Farming and the Rural Community in Ontario: An Introduction. Ed. Tony
   Fuller. Toronto: Foundation for Rural Living, 1985.

Kappel-Smith, Diana. "Pipeline in the Sugarbush." *Country Journal*, February, 1982.

Kelly, Clarence, F. "Mechanical Harvesting." *Scientific American*. August, 1967.

Ladell, John and Ladell, Monica. *A Farm in the Family*. Hamilton: Dundurn Press, 1985.

Marshall, John Ewing. *Half Century of Farming in Dufferin*. (Pamphlet, no. 32) Toronto: Ontario Archives, 1976.

————. *Fifty Years of Rural Life in Dufferin County*. (Pamphlet, no. 52) Toronto: Ontario Archives, 1977.

Neal, Carolyn O. "Ontario Barns". Published report of the third Agricultural History of Ontario Seminar. Guelph: 1978.

Ontario Agricultural Commission. *Report of the Commissioners*. 5 Vols. Toronto: C. Blackett Robinson, 1881.

Phillips, W.G. *The Agricultural Implement Industry in Canada*. Toronto: Saunders, 1970.

Reaman, G. Elmore. *A History of Agriculture in Ontario*. Two volumes. Toronto: Saunders, 1970.

Russell, Loris. *Everyday Life in Colonial Canada*. Toronto: Copp Clark Publishing, 1973.

Tait, Lyal. *Tobacco in Canada*. Tillsonburg: Ontario Flue-Cured Tobacco Growers' Marketing Board, 1968.

Walker, E.K. "Delhi Research Station 1933–1983." Historical Series, No. 17. Delhi: Research Branch, Agriculture Canada, 1983.

Index